Dear Reed,

I'm sorry. I know it was awful, running out on you like that at the last minute, but I just couldn't go through with the wedding. I know everyone has always said we're perfect for each other. I know they've been expecting us to join the family bloodlines—and the family fortunes—since the first time we waltzed together at Miss Margaret's Academy of Dance for Young Ladies and Gentlemen. I believed that was our destiny, too, until that awful moment when we were standing in front of the church with our families behind us and I suddenly realized I couldn't breathe. I know you'll think I'm being melodramatic—Great-Aunt Katherine certainly did!—but I felt as if I were suffocating, as if marriage and Boston and the weight of expectation were literally smothering me. It isn't anything you've done or not done, Reed. It's me. I need something different. I don't know what, exactly, but I've met someone—his name is Jesse—here in New Orleans who's completely unlike anyone I've ever known before....

Sincerely,

Kate

Reluctant Grooms

1. Lazarus Rising
   Anne Stuart
2. A Million Reasons Why
   Ruth Jean Dale
3. Designs on Love
   Gina Wilkins
4. The Nesting Instinct
   Elizabeth August
5. Best Man for the Job
   Dixie Browning
6. Not *His* Wedding!
   Suzanne Simms

Western Weddings

7. The Bridal Price
   Barbara Boswell
8. McCade's Woman
   Rita Rainville
9. Cactus Rose
   Stella Bagwell
10. The Cowboy and the Chauffeur
    Elizabeth August
11. Marriage-Go-Round
    Katherine Ransom
12. September Morning
    Diana Palmer

Instant Families

13. Circumstantial Evidence
    Annette Broadrick
14. Bundle of Joy
    Barbara Bretton
15. McConnell's Bride
    Naomi Horton
16. A Practical Marriage
    Dallas Schulze
17. Love Counts
    Karen Percy
18. Angel and the Saint
    Emilie Richards

Marriage, Inc.

19. Father of the Bride
    Cathy Gillen Thacker
20. Wedding of the Year
    Elda Minger
21. Wedding Eve
    Betsy Johnson
22. Taking a Chance on Love
    Gina Wilkins
23. This Day Forward
    Elizabeth Morris
24. The Perfect Wedding
    Arlene James

Make-Believe Matrimony

25. The Marriage Project
    Lynn Patrick
26. It Happened One Night
    Marie Ferrarella
27. Married?!
    Annette Broadrick
28. In the Line of Duty
    Doreen Roberts
29. Outback Nights
    Emilie Richards
30. Love for Hire
    Jasmine Cresswell

Wanted: Spouse

31. Annie in the Morning
    Curtiss Ann Matlock
32. Mail-Order Mate
    Louella Nelson
33. A Business Arrangement
    Kate Denton
34. Mail Order Man
    Roseanne Williams
35. Silent Sam's Salvation
    Myrna Temte
36. Marry Sunshine
    Anne McAllister

Runaway Brides

37. Runaway Bride
    Karen Leabo
38. Easy Lovin'
    Candace Schuler
39. Madeline's Song
    Stella Bagwell
40. Temporary Temptress
    Christine Rimmer
41. Almost a Bride
    Raye Morgan
42. Strangers No More
    Naomi Horton

Solution: Wedding

43. To Choose a Wife
    Phyllis Halldorson
44. A Most Convenient Marriage
    Suzanne Carey
45. First Comes Marriage
    Debbie Macomber
46. Make-believe Marriage
    Carole Buck
47. Once Upon a Time
    Lucy Gordon
48. Taking Savanah
    Pepper Adams

Please address questions and book requests to: Harlequin Reader Service
U.S.: 3010 Walden Ave., P.O. Box 1325, Buffalo, NY 14269
Canadian: P.O. Box 609, Fort Erie, Ont. L2A 5X3

Runaway Brides

CANDACE
SCHULER
EASY LOVIN'

Harlequin Books

TORONTO • NEW YORK • LONDON
AMSTERDAM • PARIS • SYDNEY • HAMBURG
STOCKHOLM • ATHENS • TOKYO • MILAN
MADRID • WARSAW • BUDAPEST • AUCKLAND

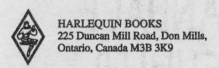

HARLEQUIN BOOKS
225 Duncan Mill Road, Don Mills,
Ontario, Canada M3B 3K9

ISBN 0-373-30138-3

EASY LOVIN'

Copyright © 1991 by Candace Schuler

Celebrity Wedding Certificates published by permission of Donald Ray Pounders from *Celebrity Wedding Ceremonies.*

Printed in U.S.A.

A Letter from the Author

Dear Reader,

It's always a pleasure for an author to have a book reprinted, but in my case the pleasure was doubled by the book chosen for the honor. The setting for *Easy Lovin'* is New Orleans, which has long held a special place in my heart, since it was a letter written about my first trip to that fabled Crescent City of Louisiana that got me started on my writing career. After reading what I had written about our vacation, my husband told me I was wasting my time writing computer manuals and said I should try writing "one of those romances you're always reading." So I did.

While *Easy Lovin'* wasn't the first book I wrote, it was one of the most fun to do. I paired an easygoing, sweet-talking Southern charmer with an uptight Yankee blue blood, added a dash of the blues, a dollop of humor and an extra big helping of the sultry Southern heat New Orleans is known for. I hope you enjoy reading Jesse and Kate's story as much as I enjoyed writing it.

Best,

Candace Schuler

**To Joe,
who took me to the Big Easy
and started it all.**

KATE HIGHTOWER slowly came awake in what she intuitively knew was a strange bed, feeling worse than she'd ever felt in her life. Little devils with little hammers were pounding on her skull from the inside. Her mouth felt as if it was stuffed with cotton batting that'd been soaked in something vile. She was feverish and damp, and an unmerciful light beat down on her closed eyelids with all the imagined heat of hell.

She moaned and started to roll over, intent on escaping the light that scorched her eyelids and bathed her world in a sea of red, but the movement hurt her head. She fell back, limp, against the pillows, and draped her forearm across her eyes to block the unrelenting light.

What on earth had happened to her?

Had she been hit by a car while crossing Boylston Street on her way to meet her mother at the dressmaker's? Fallen down the stairs at her Great-Aunt Katherine's Beacon Hill mansion and landed on her head? Been mugged while cutting through the Commons on the way to her office in the Hightower Building?

She couldn't remember anything of the sort, not the faintest glimmer of an accident, but something must have put her here. Wherever "here" was. The hospital? No, it didn't smell the least bit medicinal. Great-Aunt Katherine's seldom used front bedroom? Possibly, but the overriding fragrance of the senior Katherine Hightower's linen was of soap; the elusive fragrance of these sheets was of flowers. Carefully she drew in a breath, just enough to enable her to identify the smell. Jasmine, she thought. Then, no, not jasmine. She sniffed again. Lilac. And then it all came back to her in a blinding, unwelcome rush.

The beginning notes of the wedding march.

Her sudden, unexplainable panic.

Her mother's gasp of shock.

Great-Aunt Katherine's humph of disapproval.

Reed's look of distress.

Lilac whisking her out of the church.

The pub.

The martinis.

The plane ride.

"Oh, God," she moaned, bringing her other arm up as if to shield her face from the accusing, uncomprehending stares of her family and friends.

She'd run out on her own wedding rehearsal!

And then she'd compounded the offense by rapidly downing three—or was it four?—martinis, sitting in a noisy little pub, trying to explain to her maid of honor, to *herself*, why she'd suddenly panicked at the thought of marrying Reed.

She'd known him all her life. Their families had been friends for years—generations, really—and she and Reed had been introduced in the cradle. They'd gone to Miss Margaret's Academy of Dance for Young Ladies and Gentlemen together, they'd attended the same private schools, the same tennis camps, the same sedate parties. They knew all the same people and had the same values and tastes. They were ideally suited to each other. Everybody said so, and had been saying so for years.

But suddenly, standing there beside him at their wedding rehearsal in the church where she'd attended Sunday services for as long as she could remember, surrounded by the people they'd both known all their lives, it had seemed as if she didn't know him at all. Or, worse, knew him far too well.

"It's a trap," she'd said to Lilac, staring into the gin in her martini glass as she tried to make some sense of her uncharacteristic behavior. "My life's a trap. A stagnant pool of unending sameness, dragging me under like quicksand, smothering me. If I marry Reed, I'll never get out. I need... I don't know—" she fished the olive out of her glass with two fingers and popped it into her mouth without a thought for proper etiquette"—something," she said, chomping it between her expensively straightened teeth. "A change, maybe. Or just some time to think."

Lilac had reached out and patted her hand. "You just come on home with me, honey," she'd said in that soft, sweet drawl of hers. "You could help me get that little ol' shop ready to open," she added, referring to the lingerie boutique she was in the process of opening and into which Kate, against the advice of her family, had invested a tidy sum of money. "I know we agreed you'd be a silent partner," Lilac hurried on when Kate opened her mouth to object, "but I promise, you wouldn't have to say a word while you're paintin' dressin' rooms. It'd be a change." She squeezed Kate's hand before letting it go to pick up her drink. "And manual labor gives you lots of time to think."

It had sounded like a good idea at the time. A brilliant idea, even. Two martinis later they were on a plane bound for New Orleans, Louisiana—home of jazz, seafood gumbo and Lilac Prescott. The flight attendant had been uncommonly friendly, Kate remembered, bringing them something to eat as well as another drink or two apiece. Whether the drinks had been martinis was open to question—her memory had begun to blur by then—but she did recall a rather hilarious cab ride through deliciously soft, warm air that smelled of honeysuckle and jasmine, and an exhilarating, albeit guilty, sense of having escaped a fate worse than death.

All that remained of those feelings this morning was the guilt, which wasn't the least bit exhilarating now, and the first hangover she'd had in all the thirty years of her circumspect life.

No one in Boston would believe it.

And no one in Boston, she realized, knew where she was, either. At least, she thought, staunchly ignoring the little spurt of illicit pleasure the idea brought her, she didn't think anyone did. She didn't remember calling; not from the pub or the airport or Lilac's apartment when they finally got there. But, then, considering the condition she'd been in last night, she could have called the White House to talk to the President and not remembered it. Well, she'd better call now, she thought, dreading the idea. Just in case she hadn't already. Her parents must be worried to a frazzle, helped along, no doubt, by one of Great-Aunt Katherine's terribly well-bred tirades on their failings as the caretakers of her namesake.

Slowly, very slowly, Kate sat up. So far, so good. Nothing had fallen off. Carefully she inched her feet over the edge of the mattress, blindly pushing away the white netting that lavishly canopied the bed, and felt around for her slippers. Her toes encountered bare floor. *Where are they?* she thought peevishly as the slippers eluded her. She always placed them, just so, every night so she knew exactly where they were each morning. And then she remembered another aspect of the previous evening's escapade.

No luggage. She'd flown to New Orleans with no luggage of any kind. Not even a makeup bag.

So what had she worn to bed? She could tell she was wearing something—it was sticking to her damp, overheated body. But she could also tell it wasn't her sensible ivory satin slip, which was what logic would suggest she'd worn.

She forced her eyes open a crack. Blinding sunlight forced them closed again. She lifted her hand, palm out, positioning it between the window and her face, and tried again, peering down at herself through narrow slits. She was wearing a faded black-and-gold Saints' football jersey and—she inched the hem upward with her left hand to check—nothing else. Not panties, not the fuzzy pink socks she usually wore to bed to keep her feet warm, not even her tasteful two-carat diamond engagement ring.

Maybe I was mugged, after all, she thought hopefully, almost wishing it were true. At least then she'd have a good reason for the naked ring finger staring her in the face. But, at the moment, she didn't have the foggiest notion of what might have happened to it. As drunk as she'd been, she might well have done something stupid and symbolic, like flinging it into the Mississippi River.

You'd think a woman would remember what she'd done with the engagement ring she'd been wearing for five years, she thought, disgusted with her recalcitrant memory.

She shook her head, trying to clear it, then moaned again, clutching at it with both hands as the world began to spin. She went very still, her bare toes on the polished oak floor, her elbows carefully balanced on her knees, her head cradled tenderly in her hands, fighting the almost overwhelming urge to lose whatever she'd eaten in the past twenty-four hours.

Deep breaths, she thought, willing her stomach to relax. *Slow, deep breaths. It'll stay down. It'll—*

"Finally decided to join the land of the livin', I see," said an irritatingly cheerful voice. "I was startin' to worry about you."

Kate slit open one eye to look at the owner of that voice—her best friend since the first day of college, her maid of honor, her partner in crime, the quintessential Southern belle, Miss Lilac Prescott of Lilac Bower Plantation.

Her toenails were painted what Kate peevishly considered an unnecessarily loud shade of pink. Her slender legs were bare to a pair of dimpled knees. From there up she was covered in another of her collection of Southern Conference football jerseys, the glaring color of this one proclaiming her the property of the Louisiana State Tigers. That was as far as Kate could see without lifting her head.

"Got yourself a little ol' hangover there, don't you, honey?" Lilac said sympathetically. "Well, don't you worry yourself. I've got just the thing to fix that."

Kate moaned and stared at the floor, watching the pink-nailed toes come within inches of hers.

"Sit up straight now, honey," Lilac urged. "And drink this." A glass of something thick and red was thrust into her line of vision. "It'll make you feel much better."

"I don't want anything to drink."

"I know you don't," Lilac said soothingly. "But drink this anyway. It'll help you feel better. I promise."

Very carefully, Kate lifted her head just enough to peer at Lilac's face. A lock of dark reddish-brown hair slid across her eyes, obscuring her vision. She pushed it out of the way with the palm of her hand. "What is it?" she asked, making no move to reach for the glass.

"It's the traditional Prescott hangover cure. Mostly tomato juice. Been in the family for generations. My daddy swore by it. Now—" she grasped Kate's wrist, gently pulled her hand from her head and pressed the glass into her limp palm "—you just take it like a good girl. That's it," she said approvingly when Kate's fingers closed around the glass. "Just drink it right up."

Kate brought it to her nose and sniffed. It smelled a little like horseradish, she thought, grimacing as another memory from last night came back to her. They'd had raw oysters and fresh horseradish at some point during the previous evening. She swallowed the lump that rose in her throat and held the glass away from her. "I don't want it."

"Of course you don't," Lilac agreed, "but drink it anyway."

Kate clamped her teeth together. "I don't want—"

"Now, don't be stubborn, Kate, honey. I made it especially for you with my own two hands." She made it sound as if she'd slaved over the concoction all morning. "It'll make you feel better. Honest. Just try it."

"It'll make me sick." The smell alone threatened to nauseate her; if she drank it, she'd throw up for sure.

"One little sip," Lilac pleaded. "For me. Please?"

Kate sighed and steeled herself. "One sip," she agreed, thinking it was the fastest way to get Lilac to leave her alone so she could die in peace. Holding her breath, she lifted the glass to her mouth and took a tiny sip, barely wetting her lips. Her stomach rumbled protestingly.

"All of it," Lilac said, putting two fingers on the bottom of the glass to keep it tilted as Kate started to hand it back. "That's right, drink it all down, honey," she said, gently forcing Kate to do just that or end up with tomato juice all over herself. Some dribbled down her chin anyway. "There now." Lilac took the glass as Kate frantically pushed it away. "That wasn't so bad, was it?"

Kate clamped her hand over her mouth and bolted to her feet, her eyes wild and accusing.

Lilac stepped out of the way. "Bathroom's right through there," she said complacently, pointing. "I'll be in the kitchen fixin' you some tea and dry toast when you come out."

THIRTY MINUTES LATER, after having emptied her stomach, brushed her teeth, swallowed three aspirin tablets and showered until the water turned cold, Kate tightened the sash on her borrowed robe, slicked back her wet hair and entered Lilac's small, sunny kitchen to find her hostess cutting toasted bread into triangles.

Lilac smiled at her as she sat down at the little white wrought-iron table. "Feelin' better?" she asked, placing a delicate china cup in front of her guest. Fragrant steam rose invitingly from its liquid surface.

"No thanks to you," Kate grumbled, cautiously waiting to see if the smell would trigger another bout of the dry heaves. When it didn't she wrapped both hands around the cup and lifted it to her mouth to take a tiny, testing sip. The tea was hot and strong and sweetened with honey, just the way she liked it. She took a bigger swallow and waited a moment. It stayed down. She looked at Lilac, no longer contemplating murder by the foulest means possible. "What was in that drink you gave me, anyway? Ipecac?"

Lilac shook her tousled blond head. "Tomato juice, a few herbs, a raw egg, a little beer." She put a plate of toast triangles in the center of the table and slipped into the seat across from Kate. "It's a Southern folk remedy—" she took a sip of tea "—based on the theory that the hair of the dog that bit you is the best cure for a hangover."

"The dog that savaged me, you mean." Kate picked up a piece of toast and stared at it, wondering if it would stay down, too. "I never felt worse in my whole life."

Lilac peered into her friend's face. "But you're feelin' better now, aren't you?"

Kate considered that for a moment. Yes, unlikely as it seemed, she *was* feeling better. The aspirin and shower and, maybe, Lilac's family remedy had helped immeasurably. Her headache had settled down to a dull throb, her mouth no longer tasted like a sewer and she was actually contemplating eating when, just thirty short minutes ago, she'd have sworn she never wanted to look at food again.

"I guess I'm going to live after all." She lifted the toast to her mouth and took a small bite, bringing the bare ring finger of her left hand into her line of vision. "If Reed or my parents don't kill me, that is."

"Don't worry," Lilac soothed, reaching out to pat her hand. "They don't know where you are."

"I didn't call, then?" She didn't think she had. *Damn.*

Lilac shook her head. "Nope."

Kate sighed. No way around it. She was going to have to call. Soon. Her parents. Reed. They'd be worrying themselves sick about her. And with good reason. She'd never just disappeared before. She'd never even been so much as ten minutes late for anything without letting someone know where she was.

As soon as I've finished breakfast, I'll call, she promised herself. She'd call her parents first, to let them know she hadn't been carried off by white slavers, then she'd call the airline to book a flight to Boston. She wouldn't call Reed, though, she decided suddenly. She'd go see him as soon as she got home; what she had to say to him was best said in person.

She spread her fingers and gazed at her hand. "I don't suppose you'd happen to know what I did with my engagement ring?" It would be nice to be able to give Reed's ring back to him when she canceled the wedding.

"It's in my purse."

Relief flooded through her. She hadn't done something stupid like fling it into the Mississippi, after all. "Really?"

"Uh-huh. You took it off on the plane and gave it to me. Said you didn't feel right wearin' it anymore."

"I don't," Kate agreed. "And yet . . . I don't know." She looked at her hand. It was slender and long-fingered, the bare nails buffed to a high shine, the skin fine-grained and pale, with a faint mark where the ring had been for the past five years. "My hand looks kind of bare without it, don't you think?"

Lilac looked at her own ringless left hand. "You'll get used to it in no time," she said sagely, speaking from the experience of having been married and divorced—through no fault of her own, of course!—twice before she was twenty-eight.

Kate sighed. "Yes, I suppose I will." She lifted her teacup, draining it, and stood up with the air of determination that was second nature to her. "I'd better call the airport and find out when the next flight to Boston is. I don't want—"

Lilac stopped her with a hand on her arm. "You're not goin' back?" she said, scandalized.

"Yes, of course. I have to."

"Why do you have to?" Lilac wanted to know.

"Well, I've got to cancel the wedding, and—" she waved her free hand distractedly "—and explain to Reed."

"Explain it to him over the phone."

"Lilac, this isn't the kind of thing you can explain over the phone. I have to do it in person, make him understand why I can't marry him."

"Uh-huh," Lilac scoffed. "And while you're explainin', Reed and your mama and daddy and that whole passel of relatives of yours'll be talkin' you into doin' what's *expected* of you, just like they did in the first place."

"No one talked me into anything." No one ever talked a Hightower into anything.

"Uh-huh," Lilac said again. "Just like they didn't talk you into changin' your major back to business administration," she said shrewdly, reminding Kate of the family crisis she'd perpetrated when, in her sophomore year, she'd wanted to switch to art history.

"There wasn't any future in art history," Kate said, recalling the argument—the very sound argument—that had been used to convince her to see reason all those years ago.

"And just like they didn't talk you into workin' in your father's law office every spring break instead of goin' to Fort Lauderdale with the rest of us."

"It was good experience."

"Well, so would Fort Lauderdale have been."

"Lilac . . ." Kate said warningly. They'd had this argument before, countless times, and had finally agreed to disagree on the subject of Kate's family.

"Well, it would have been," Lilac insisted. "And besides, you wanted to go."

"Maybe," Kate agreed, "but it hasn't got anything to do with going home to explain to Reed."

"It has *everythin'* to do with it!" Lilac said earnestly. "If you go back they're all just goin' to start right in to harpin' about tradition and how perfect they think Reed is for you and how marryin' him would bring two family fortunes together. Just like they did in the first place. *And*, I might add, they're also goin' to take every opportunity to remind you that your ol' biological clock is tickin' away."

"You're exaggerating."

"I am not," Lilac said indignantly. "That old dragon you call an aunt pointed it out to me several times. 'I'm so glad to see our dear Katherine getting married before she's too old to have children,' she said. And that's an exact quote."

Kate didn't have an answer for that. She knew it was probably true; Great-Aunt Katherine had said the same thing to her more than once. And, having reached her thirtieth birthday not too long ago, she had thought about it a few times herself. "Well, they still didn't talk me into anything," she said firmly. "I wanted to marry Reed."

Lilac lifted a delicate eyebrow. "So what are you doin' here?"

"I...well, I..." No answer was immediately forthcoming. What *was* she doing here? "I changed my mind?" she ventured uncertainly. Indecisiveness wasn't something she had very much experience with—it wasn't encouraged in a Hightower. But, then, she'd done a lot of things in the past twenty-four hours she didn't have a lot of experience with. And after all, anyone could change their mind.

That being the case, one thing stood out clearly: if she'd changed her mind once, she could change it again. Especially with her entire family oh-so-subtly pressuring her to make the "right" decision. Hightowers might not get talked into things, but they weren't above being made to see the error of their ways if it was pointed out often enough. And her family would certainly point it out. Repeatedly. She sank back into her chair. "So what now?"

"Now you call your mama and daddy and tell 'em
you need some time to think about your life and that
you're goin' to stay and visit with me while you do it,"
Lilac said, having already thought the whole thing
through. "Tell 'em you need to stay down here awhile
and make sure your investment is safe."

"My investment *is* safe," Kate said firmly, meaning
it. Lilac had been a business major, too, effortlessly
making the straight A's Kate had had to sweat bullets
for. She'd thoroughly and competently researched
everything from market trends to the annual reports
of similar businesses to the reliability of possible sup-
pliers before deciding on a lingerie boutique. And then
she'd drawn up a five-year plan that would make any
corporate controller weep with envy. "There's no way
Secrets is going to be anything but a raging success,"
Kate assured her best friend.

Lilac's mouth turned up in a wry smile. "Try tellin'
that to your family," she said. "And then call Reed and
tell him you're not goin' home to marry him." She
brushed her dainty, pink-nailed hands together, dust-
ing off the crumbs, and stood up. "And then get
dressed so we can go shoppin'."

"Shopping?" *At a time like this?*

"Of course. You can't go runnin' around New Orleans—" she pronounced it as one word, *Nu-awlins*
"—in the suit you wore down here, honey."

"I can't?"

"'Course not." She picked up both empty teacups and carried them to the sink. "It'd be way too hot. You're goin' to need some sundresses and sandals. A couple pairs of lightweight slacks. Some cotton blouses. Besides, you spilled coffee on your skirt last night at the Café du Monde. Go on and call now," Lilac said, when Kate just sat there, staring at her. "Phone's in the bedroom."

HER MOTHER REACTED about as Kate expected her to. "Aunt Katherine is quite put out about your behavior. We all are," she said. But Kate knew it was her great-aunt's displeasure that bothered her mother most. All the Hightowers—from the smallest cousin right on up to Kate's father—had a healthy respect for the oldest living Hightower's well-bred wrath. "Your father was so upset he went to his office early today. He didn't even have breakfast first."

Probably trying to avoid Aunt Katherine, Kate thought. *I don't blame him.*

"I don't know what we're going to tell everyone," the voice on the other end of the line went on fretfully.

"Why don't you let Mrs. Myers handle it, Mother," Kate suggested. Barbara Myers was the wedding consultant who'd been hired to orchestrate the grand event. "She made all the arrangements, so she can just as easily cancel them."

"Yes, that's true. She did, didn't she?" Her mother's voice brightened a bit. "And I'm sure she's run into this sort of . . . of thing—" her tone made it sound like a perverted act "—before, so she'll know just what to say when she calls everyone to postpone the wedding."

"Not postpone, Mother," Kate corrected her. "Cancel."

"We'll see, dear," said Frances Hightower.

Reed reacted about as she'd expected him to, as well. Although he tried to disguise it, she could tell by his voice he was annoyed—not that she blamed him!—but he didn't seem to take her panicked flight a whit more seriously than her mother had. "This is just a severe case of the pre-wedding jitters, Kate, and you'll realize that when you've had time to think about it. Take as long as you need," he said understandingly. "I'll be waiting."

Kate was thankful that he hadn't made a fuss, of course, but, as she hung up the phone, she couldn't help wishing he hadn't been quite so all-fired understanding and unemotional, so . . . so predictable—That, just this once, he'd forget himself enough to come charging down to New Orleans in a jealous rage and drag her back by the hair or tell her to go to hell or *something!*

But he hadn't. And he wouldn't. And that's what made him Reed—the man who, until yesterday, she'd been planning to spend the rest of her life with. It was enough, as Lilac would say, to give a body the heebie-jeebies.

2

"I'M NOT GOING into one more store," Kate declared stubbornly, stopping on the narrow sidewalk of the seven-hundred block of Royal Street as Lilac reached out to push open yet another shop door. This one was a pale pastel pink with the word IMAGES artistically scrawled across it in flowing burgundy script. "I've got enough stuff here—" she lifted both hands, laden with bulging shopping bags "—to stock my own store."

Lilac grabbed her sleeve. "This isn't a store," she said, dragging her through the door. "It's a beauty salon."

"Beauty salon?" Kate looked around quickly as they entered, taking in the lacy ferns, the white leather furniture and the silver-framed pictures of beautifully coiffed women that graced the pale pink walls of the reception area. "What are we doing in a beauty salon?"

"What do people usually do in a beauty salon?" Lilac asked as she moved toward the woman who was coming around a chest-high counter to greet them. She was young and pretty, with long tanned legs barely covered by a white denim miniskirt and a soft pink T-shirt with the salon's name emblazoned across the chest in burgundy letters.

"Lilac, what a surprise!" she said, reaching out to embrace her. "I didn't see your name in the appointment book for today."

"It isn't." Lilac returned the embrace with one arm while keeping her other hand firmly anchored to Kate's sleeve. "Kate, honey, this is my second cousin on my mama's side, Annabelle Jamison," she said, drawing away from the younger woman as she made the introductions. "Annabelle, I'd like you to meet Katherine Hightower, a friend from college. She wants to get a haircut. Is Jesse in today?"

"He's in the back finishing a perm." Annabelle moved around the counter and ran a beautifully manicured finger down a column in the open appointment book. "I don't think he has any free time today, though."

"I don't want a haircut," Kate hissed in Lilac's ear.

Lilac ignored her and leaned over the counter to look for herself. "Nothin' at all?" she asked. "Not even twenty minutes or so for a consultation, at least? We could come back for the haircut later."

"Well, maybe." Annabelle tapped the appointment book. "It looks like he might have a free half hour or so before his next appointment. The perm didn't take as long as it was scheduled for, and his next appointment is Miz Barclay. She's always late." An-

nabelle looked up with a smile. "He might fit you in.
I'll go ask him."

"I don't want a haircut," Kate said again, a little
louder, as Annabelle came around the counter.

Lilac motioned her to hush. "Tell him I'd really appreciate it if he could do me this one teeny, tiny little
favor," she said to Annabelle as she moved toward the
trellised arch that led into the busy main room of the
salon. "Kate really needs a pick-me-up, and I'd be
eternally grateful."

"I don't want a haircut," Kate said again, more
forcefully, when the receptionist was out of earshot.
She wasn't used to being ignored or having her clearly
expressed wishes overridden. She was also hot, thirsty
and tired. Shopping—the way Lilac did it—was hard
work, especially when you weren't feeling up to par
to start with. "I like my hair just fine the way it is."

Lilac fixed her with a look that made her feel as if
she'd just been caught in a lie by one of the nuns at Our
Lady. "Did you or did you not—less than thirty short
minutes ago, mind you—stand in the dressin' room
at the Dixie Rose Boutique in your underwear and say
you wished you could think of somethin' different to
do with your hair?"

"Well, yes." She'd said something vaguely along
those lines. "But . . ."

Lilac's eyebrow lifted. "Well, then?"

"I didn't mean that I wanted to do it right now."

"No time like the present. And look—" she waved her free hand toward the back of the salon "—Jesse's free."

Kate looked. And then couldn't look away. Sauntering toward them through the noisy bustle of the salon was the sexiest man she'd ever seen in her life.

He was lean and loose-limbed, with the elegant, slow-moving grace of a prowling cougar. His hair was the tousled, tawny blond of a California surfer, irresistibly tempting to feminine fingertips. His skin was smooth and sleekly golden, with a glow that suggested the warmth of lazy summer afternoons spent in bed. His smile, answering those of his female customers as he made his meandering way between the stylists' chairs, was slow, inviting and playful, lighting up his eyes with a sensual promise.

And such eyes! Kate thought, feeling their power right down to the toes of her sensible, low-heeled beige pumps. They were a deep, hypnotic blue, with a slightly dangerous, slightly decadent, knowing gleam that said he was just the man to make all your erotic dreams come true, if only you were brave enough to let him.

Even his clothes, as casual as they were, managed to add to his aura of laid-back sexuality. His pale pink Images T-shirt, the color emphasizing rather than compromising his masculinity, showcased a finely muscled chest and a stomach that was washboard flat. It disappeared into the waistband of a pair of pleated-front, fashionably baggy white linen slacks that made a woman wonder what he'd look like in a pair of skin-tight Levi's—or nothing at all.

Kate could hear the hearts flutter from where she stood. She pressed a hand to her chest to make sure hers wasn't one of them. It was.

Ridiculous, she thought, staring at him as he closed the small space left between them. *He's not even my type!*

But she knew she lied. A man like the one ambling toward her was every woman's type at least once in her life. If she was lucky. The thought popped into her head before she could censor it. Kate flushed and looked away nervously, as embarrassed as if she'd spoken out loud. Out of the corner of her eye, she watched his lazy smile flash as he greeted the woman still clutching the sleeve of her dress.

"Lilac, darlin', what a delightful surprise." His drawl was as slow and sexy as he was, fairly dripping with Southern charm.

He reached out to take Lilac's hands in his as he spoke. She let go of Kate's sleeve to give them to him.

"I haven't seen your pretty face in a month of Sundays. Not since Aimée and Jack's anniversary party." He bent to kiss her on each cheek, taking his time about it, and then straightened. "What brings you to Images on this fine summer day?" he asked, gazing down at her as if her answer were the only thing in the world that could possibly interest him right now.

Neither woman caught his quick, assessing look in Kate's direction.

She was standing stiffly, gazing past him into the salon. Her face was delicately flushed—from the heat, he thought—giving needed color to her cool, patrician features. She had lovely, arched eyebrows and long lashes shielding eyes of a color he couldn't see. Her makeup was minimal, nothing more than mascara and a bit of lip gloss. But it was more than enough; she had the fine porcelain skin of a baby and the unexpectedly lush mouth of a courtesan.

"I was hopin' you could fit Kate in for a quick haircut," Lilac said, pulling his attention back to her without ever knowing she'd lost it. "She's just been through a major upheaval in her life and—"

"Lilac!" Kate admonished, thinking that Lilac was about to blurt out every embarrassing thing that had happened.

Lilac made an exaggerated moue. "Oh, don't worry, Kate. I wasn't goin' to say anythin' indiscreet. I'm the very soul of discretion when it's necessary." She fluttered her lashes at the man still holding her hands in his. "Isn't that right, Jesse?"

"The very soul of discretion," he agreed with a wink, flirting right back at her. But his mind was elsewhere.

Her eyes are brown, he thought, trying not to stare too obviously. Deep, rich brown, as soft and sweet as chocolate that had been left to melt in the sun. They

were also very nearly on a level with his own. Which,
he estimated, would make her about five feet eight,
judging by his own six feet and—he lowered his gaze
to check—the low-heeled shoes she was wearing. She
had the kind of body that went with her regal height,
too—a full-breasted, small-waisted, curvy-hipped
figure that was meant to wear feminine, fitted dresses
and low-cut tops that showed off her lush propor-
tions.

The dress she was wearing had definite possibili-
ties, he decided. The soft apricot color was just right
with her warm, creamy coloring. It was pulled in by
a narrow leather belt, showing off her waist, but she
needed to roll up the sleeves a bit and unbutton a button or two down the front. The way she was wearing
it now, with the sleeves cuffed at her wrists and the
bodice buttoned up to the soft hollow of her throat,
she looked as prim as a Baptist missionary.

He smiled slightly, amused at the fanciful simile,
just as their eyes met again. It seemed, for just
that precise moment, as if they were sharing...
something. Jesse's smile widened a bit, telegraphing
awareness and a sort of teasing invitation—*How 'bout
we get to know each other better*—with just a wry
twist of his lips and the sudden gleam in his
blue eyes.

Kate's errant heart began to flutter even faster. *God,
he's gorgeous!* she thought as her eyes skittered past
his shoulder again, pretending what was going on in

the salon behind him was the most fascinating thing she'd ever seen. That's when she noticed the tiny diamond earring glittering in his left earlobe.

She stiffened, the corners of her mouth tightening in a way that would remind anyone who knew them both of Great-Aunt Katherine at her most disapproving. *Most definitely not my type,* she thought, trying to believe it. Any man who'd wear an earring probably flouted a whole host of other social conventions on a regular basis. Kate was a woman who, until yesterday, had never flouted even the least of them.

Definitely the missionary type, Jesse thought again, still smiling at her. Except for that courtesan's mouth. It was, he decided, a damned intriguing combination. He wondered what the recent major upheaval in her life had been and if that's what made her hold herself in so tightly, or if the primness he sensed was natural to her. It would be interesting to find out. Interesting to see if it was her mouth or her manner that lied.

"She doesn't want anythin' drastic," Lilac was saying, chattering on as if she had his full attention. "Just a little change to lift her spirits." Her lashes fluttered again. "Can you fit her in?"

"Nothing would give me more pleasure," he said, blithely disregarding the fact that he'd have to forgo his lunch to do so. He turned to the receptionist hovering at his elbow. "Call Miz Barclay, Annabelle, darlin', and ask her if she could be a little later than usual. Then get these two lovely ladies a glass of iced tea. With mint. And lots of sugar for Lilac." He looked at Kate. "Do you take sugar in your iced tea, Miz...?"

"Oh, lordy, how thoughtless of me!" Lilac said before Kate could answer him. "I've completely forgotten my manners. Jesse, I'd like you to meet one of my dearest friends, Katherine Hightower," she said, swiftly rectifying the omission. "Kate, honey, this is Jesse de Vallerin, the best hairstylist in New Orleans."

Kate extended her hand politely. Generations of good breeding would allow her to do nothing less, and besides, she had a burning desire to see if his honey-gold skin was as warm as it looked. It was. "I'm very pleased to meet you, Mr. de Vallerin," she said, feeling the heat spread all the way up her arm.

"Jesse, please. And the pleasure is all mine." The smile that accompanied his words would have led a lesser woman to believe he meant them literally. "Entirely all mine," he said. His other hand came up to join the first, cradling hers between them for a moment before letting it go. "Now, then, do you take sugar in your tea?"

"No." Kate's voice was uncharacteristically soft. She tried to inject a little more Hightower steel into it. "No, I don't take sugar, thank you."

"No sugar for Miz Hightower, Annabelle. Here—" he reached for the shopping bags that still dangled from Kate's arms "—let me take those for you." He placed them on the reception counter. "Annabelle'll take care of them just as soon as she's brought your tea." He turned to Kate and Lilac, putting a hand on the small of each woman's back.

Kate felt his heat seep into her spine, softening it.

"You two come right on over here and set yourselves down," he said, steering them into the main room of the salon.

As if she had no will of her own, Kate allowed herself to be escorted to a burgundy stylist's chair in front of a mirrored wall. With just the slightest pressure on her shoulder, he pushed her down. She sat, telling herself it was only because of the promised tea— something cold and wet would taste heavenly—and the chance to get off her feet for a moment. Certainly not because she had any intention of letting him do anything to her hair.

He pulled a tall stool within talking range of the stylist's chair. "You park your pretty little self right here, Lilac, darlin'," he said, patting it. "Now—" he turned back to Kate, his hands going to the wide gold clip that held her hair in a ponytail at the nape of her neck "—let's see what we've got here."

Before she could utter a word of protest, he'd dropped the clip in her lap and was fluffing her hair over her shoulders. Fingers spread wide, palms curved against her scalp, he ran his hands under her hair from nape to crown, then moved them out slowly, letting the silky strands drift down.

It felt so wonderful, she almost moaned with pleasure.

"You've got a good basic cut already." He rubbed a few strands between his thumb and index finger. "Excellent condition, too." He lifted her hair again, sifting it through his fingers almost lovingly. Once. Twice. A third time.

Without conscious volition, Kate's head lolled forward a bit and she closed her eyes, relishing the soothing motion of his talented hands. The nagging little headache left over from the morning began to melt away as if by magic.

"You take good care of it."

Kate's "Hmm" of agreement was almost a purr.

"Lovely color," he murmured. "Just on the edge of being auburn. Virgin?"

Kate's head snapped up, her startled eyes meeting his in the mirror. "I beg your pardon?"

"Virgin?" he asked again, thinking she simply hadn't heard him.

Kate continued to stare uncomprehendingly, wondering if he could possibly be asking her what she thought he was.

A smile curved his lips. A slow, seductive, knowing smile that crinkled up the corners of his eyes and made him look as if he was focusing on her face across a rumpled pillow. "Your hair, darlin'," he drawled teasingly, realizing what she'd thought he meant. "Is it colored?"

"Oh." He was asking about her hair! "No—" she willed herself not to blush "—no, it's natural."

He sifted it through his fingers again, slowly, letting it drift down to her shoulders once more. "Permed?" His eyes—blue, hypnotic, brimming with his own brand of sleepy sensuality—held hers in the mirror.

Kate had to fight the cowardly urge to look away. "No," she said. "The wave's natural, too."

He nodded as if in agreement and then, still holding her eyes in the mirror, ran the flat of his hand over her hair from the roots to the ends, smoothing it into place. It was beautiful hair. Soft. Silky. Glowing with health and conscientious care. He wondered what it would look like spread out across his pillow.

Kate went stock-still as he smoothed her hair, unable to look away, fighting the insane urge to rub against his hand like a cat being stroked.

"Here's your tea, honey." Lilac's pink-nailed hand, holding a tall glass of mint-scented iced tea, appeared practically under her nose.

She reached to take it, thankful for an excuse to break eye contact with the man standing behind her. "Thank you," she said, keeping her eyes protectively lowered as she sipped it.

"Thank Annabelle," Lilac advised, sitting down on her stool. She took a sip of her tea. "Well, what do you think?" she said to Jesse.

"About what?" he asked absently, still mesmerized by thoughts of Kate's hair spread out on his pillow...trailing over his chest...tickling his stomach.

Lilac flapped her free hand at Kate. "About her hair, of course. What are we talkin' about here?"

He pulled himself together with an effort. "Of course. Her hair. Well..." Unable to resist, he smoothed a hand down its shining length again. "It doesn't need much. Slight layering, I'd say. Right around the front. Through here." He fluffed it a bit at the temples to show them what he meant. "And a little through the crown to give it some lift and release more of the natural curl. And then some subtle highlighting around the face to bring out the red a bit. Here—" he lifted a few strands to illustrate "—and here." He captured Kate's eyes in the mirror again. "How's that sound, darlin'?"

"It sounds fine," Kate said, completely forgetting that, not only had she not wanted a haircut when she came in, but doing anything to "bring out the red" had always been close to last on her list of things to do.

"Good." He smiled at her, pleased.

"Have you got time for all that?" Lilac asked, reminding them both he had a full schedule.

Kate tensed, waiting for his answer. She suddenly wanted a haircut and highlights and whatever else he suggested very much.

"Michele can shampoo her for me," Jesse said, juggling appointments in his head as he spoke. "I'll do the cut, then—" He turned slightly. "Annabelle, darlin', bring me the schedule book, would you, please?"

Annabelle hurried over with it.

"Didi can do a manicure, on the house," he said, his eyes on the schedule book, "while I'm doing Miz Barclay, then I can do the highlights after that." He looked up. "How's that sound?" He wanted, very much, for it to sound all right to the prim, brown-eyed beauty in his stylist's chair.

"Sounds perfect," Lilac said before Kate could say that it sounded perfect to her, too. "Nothin' like a lot of pamperin' to cheer a woman up." She got to her feet, suddenly all bustling action, and put her half-full glass of tea on the stool. "I'll just take all your packages home, Kate, honey, then come back and get you at—" she glanced at her watch "—three-thirty?"

"Better make it four," Jesse said, before Kate could answer.

"Four, then." She leaned over, pressing a quick kiss on Kate's cheek. "Just relax and let Jesse take care of you," she advised brightly. "He knows just what to do to make a woman feel real good."

3

"I DON'T KNOW what made me say yes." Clad in an ivory-colored lace-trimmed bra and half slip, a pair of panty hose dangling from one hand, Kate moved between the open doors of the rosewood armoire that had been cleared out for her use and Lilac's immense French Victorian tester bed. A small pile of discarded clothes lay across the foot of the big bed, silently marking her uncharacteristic indecision. "I mean, there I was, sitting in the chair one minute, talking about how red he thought I should let him go with the highlights—" She paused, her gaze caught by her reflection in the cheval mirror by the bed.

The changes had seemed harmless enough when Jesse had suggested them; a little artfully random highlighting around her face—to "play up your lovely eyes," he'd said; a bit of layering to add "a little fullness" to her basic style. It was subtle, and yet . . .

"You don't think it's too red, do you?" she asked, holding a strand of her newly highlighted hair away from her temple.

"Looks absolutely lovely," Lilac said, her head bent as she sat scrunched up in the middle of the white lace bedspread with a baby-blue towel under her foot, applying a light, lavender-pink polish to her toenails.

"Not too, oh, I don't know—" she fluffed the lightly layered hair at the crown, tilting her head this way and that to better assess the changes "—too brassy or wild looking?"

"You couldn't look wild if you tried," Lilac soothed, sticking one leg out in front of her to study the new color. Satisfied, she carefully replaced the brush in the small bottle balanced on her bent knee. "What happened then?" she asked, batting white netting out of the way as she leaned over to set the bottle on the bedside table.

"What happened then, when?" Kate said, still studying her new hairdo in the mirror. She liked the cut, she decided; the extra bit of fullness made her face look thinner and even a touch exotic. And the highlights, well, they might grow on her, given enough time.

"You were sittin' in the chair—" Lilac stuck both legs out in front of her, carefully crossed her ankles and leaned back on her elbows "—talkin' about your hair, and then?"

"And then I found myself agreeing to have dinner with him tonight as easily as if I'd been hypnotized or...or something." She turned to face her hostess, her hands lifting in an exasperated gesture that sent the legs of the panty hose she was holding fluttering in front of her face. "I don't know what came over me."

But she did. Sort of. It was that look in his eyes, that playfully seductive, sensually promising, thoroughly masculine look. She'd never seen it in any other man's eyes before, at least not directed at her, she hadn't, and it intrigued her more than anything had in a long time. But it wasn't something she could admit—the fact that she'd been seduced out of her customary good sense by the look in a man's eyes— not even to herself.

"What came over you is that potent Southern charm we're all so famous for down here," Lilac said smugly, knowing exactly what had come over her friend and not the least bit shy about saying so. "Jesse's got more than his share, is all, and it can be sort of overwhelmin' if you're not used to it."

"But he's not even my type!" Kate said, amazed— *appalled* was more like it—at her reaction to Jesse de Vallerin's lethal, blue-eyed Southern charm.

Lilac's grin was sly and knowing. "Honey, that man is every woman's type."

Kate's eyes narrowed with something she refused to recognize as jealousy. It was, after all, exactly what she'd thought herself when she first laid eyes on him. Still, she couldn't help but ask. "Yours, too?"

"Lordy, no!" Lilac managed to look scandalized at the very thought. "Not that he wouldn't be if he were anybody else, mind you. He's got a very—" her eyebrows lifted, making her look like a wicked imp "—interestin' way about him that tends to make a woman wonder what he'd be like in bed. Not to mention the cutest little backside in the state of Louisiana. Which, I might add, is known for great male backsides. Most all our boys play football from the time they're real little," she offered by way of explanation. "And it does wonderful things for the male physique. But Jesse and I've known each other since we were kids. Why, his middle sister, Ginny—that's short for Geneviève—was my very best friend when I was growin' up. Jesse used to fix our hair for us before a big date. Down here, that makes us practically related." She cocked her head consideringly. "Matter of fact, I think we *are* related, way back somewhere. There's a de Vallerin lady in the Prescott family tree— three, maybe four, generations back. She married my great-grand-daddy's younger brother, I think. Or maybe it was his—"

"Lilac," Kate said, making no effort to keep the exasperation out of her voice.

The blue eyes widened innocently. "What?"

"I'm sure your family history is very interesting but I'm supposed to be getting dressed for a—" Kate stumbled over the word, as if it were hard to say "—a date, remember?"

"Well, you just go right on ahead." Lilac waved a languid hand. "I'm certainly not stoppin' you."

"You aren't helping me, either."

"I don't recall you askin' for my help," Lilac said but she scooted across the mattress, careful not to smear her polish on the lace spread, and got to her feet. "But here I am—" she took the panty hose from Kate as she spoke, casually adding them to the pile of clothes on the foot of her bed "—ready and willin' to be of service in your time of need."

Kate's answering smile was a bit distracted. "Thanks," she said, reaching for the tailored white slacks she'd bought that afternoon. "I need all the help I can get." She turned toward the cheval mirror and held the slacks up in front of her. Maybe with her navy linen blazer, she thought. And then, no, she remembered, her navy linen blazer, along with her navy wool flannel blazer and her heavier navy melton blazer, was hanging on a wooden hanger in her cedar-lined closet in Boston. "What do you think?" she asked, looking at Lilac in the mirror. "Maybe with the cotton sweater I bought at the Dixie Rose?"

Lilac shook her head. The sweater in question was buttercup yellow, comfortably oversize, with a large white flower woven into the front. "Too casual for a first date."

"*Only* date," Kate corrected.

"Not if you play your cards right." Lilac took the slacks from Kate and tossed them onto the bed behind her, ignoring the admonishing look Kate sent her way. "What time is he pickin' you up?"

"He said seven-thirty." Which, she thought, judging by the fact that she hadn't seen him move faster than a slow amble all afternoon, undoubtedly meant he'd show up closer to eight o'clock. Or even eight-thirty.

"Well, then, you'd better shake your tail, honey," Lilac said. "Jesse's always real punctual."

Kate made a small sound of disbelief as she turned toward the armoire. Jesse's type—the casual, devil-may-care type—was *always* late.

"Jesse might look like he's movin' slow, but he always gets where he's goin'," Lilac informed her. "Usually before everybody else, too."

Kate didn't even glance around. "And the Pope is Jewish," she scoffed.

"All right, don't believe me. I'm not the one Jesse's gonna catch runnin' around in her unmentionables. Not," she added, "that havin' Jesse catch you half-naked would be all that bad, but—"

Kate turned to look at her friend. "You're serious."

It was Lilac's turn to look exasperated. "Of course, I'm serious. I'm not just talkin' to hear the sound of my own voice, you know."

Kate's gaze dropped to the slim gold watch on her left wrist. "It's already five after," she said, feeling a sudden, unnerving sense of panic. Here she'd thought she had plenty of time and now— She sent a skittering, indecisive glance from the pile of clothes on the bed to the ones still hanging in the armoire. If she'd

been in Boston, if she were dressing for a date with
Reed, she'd know exactly what to wear. Not knowing made her feel strangely out of control. It wasn't a
feeling she liked. "You said you'd help me decide what
to wear!"

Lilac grinned. The Kate she'd known since they'd
shared a dorm room at college was always calm and
cool and never at a loss for the right thing to do or say
or wear. It was kind of endearing to see her in a feminine flutter over a man she said wasn't even her type.

Kate glared at her grinning friend. "Well, are you
going to help me or not?"

"Why, of course, honey lamb." She reached up and
patted Kate's cheek. "What are friends for?" She
turned and pulled a garment out of the discarded pile
of clothes on the bed. "This one." She held up a dress
Kate had already decided against. It was a deliciously feminine confection of a dress, made of lined
eyelet cotton the color of a frozen mint daiquiri. De-
signed with a halter-style top, it had a tight waist, a
full skirt and a self-ruffled hem that ended at midcalf.
"It's perfect," Lilac said.

"For you, maybe." Kate snatched it away from her
and held it up by the straps, head tilted as she scowled
at her reflection in the mirror. Pretty as the color was,
the style was entirely too frilly. It would require her
to go braless—something she very seldom did because of the way she was built. Or overbuilt, as Great-
Aunt Katherine had said more than once. It would

also leave her back almost entirely bare above the waist. She should've known Lilac would pick it over everything else they'd bought today. "I don't know why I let you talk me into buying it," she said, shaking her head. "It's nothing like I usually wear."

"Which is exactly why you decided to buy it, if I recall. You said you needed a change, remember?"

"No, *you* said I needed a change, and I was just too tired to argue. Here—" she tossed it to Lilac "—you take it if you like it so much."

"I don't have what it takes to fill it out," Lilac said regretfully, laying it on the bed. "And the color would look dreadful on me." She smoothed a hand over the fabric. "But it's perfect for you."

"No, it's not." Kate turned to the armoire and, after a moment's consideration, pulled out one of the two remaining dresses. A crisp cotton piqué sheath in oyster-white, it was trimmed around the neck and armholes with a narrow, honey-colored cord. The lightweight, buttonless jacket that went with it was just the opposite—honey-colored with oyster trim. Of all the things she'd purchased today, it was the most like what she wore back home in Boston. "This is perfect for me," she said suddenly decisive.

Lilac gave an unladylike snort of disapproval. "If you're goin' to church."

Deliberately ignoring her, Kate ran an assessing eye over the three pairs of shoes she'd purchased during the morning's wild shopping spree. A pair of strappy white sandals, white canvas tennis shoes and the low-heeled beige pumps she'd slipped on immediately after she bought them stood side-by-side on a low shelf in the armoire next to the dark brown leather pumps she'd been wearing when she fled Boston. The beige pumps, she decided. The sandals were just a shade too bright and frivolous for the oyster-white sheath. *But they'd be perfect with the eyelet sundress*. Kate ignored the stray thought as deliberately as she'd ignored Lilac's comment.

"You're not really goin' to wear that outfit, are you?" Lilac demanded as Kate turned from the armoire with the dress over her arm and the beige pumps in her hand.

"Yes, I really am," she said calmly. Having finally made a decision about what to wear seemed to have settled her nerves. She laid the dress over the other clothes on the bed, sat down next to it and bent over to place the shoes on the floor. "Why shouldn't I?"

"Because Jesse's bound to take you to the Quarter, for one thing, and that dress is more suited to a ladies' auxiliary luncheon than a Friday night in the— Lordy, Kate, you're goin' to roast alive in those," she said as Kate reached for her panty hose. "And you don't need that slip you've got on, either. That dress is lined, isn't it?" She flipped up the hem to check. "Yes, it is," she informed Kate. "It's over eighty-five degrees out there, in case you hadn't noticed, and humid as all get out, too. No sense in wearin' any more than you have to."

"It gets nearly as hot in Boston," Kate said, smoothing the silky nylon fabric over her calves. "And I manage to wear hose without roasting alive. And a slip."

"In an air-conditioned office," Lilac agreed, "or that mausoleum of your great-aunt's," she added, recalling how she'd nearly frozen to death at the bridal tea the elder Katherine Hightower had given for her great-niece. "But, like I said, Jesse's bound to take you to the Quarter for dinner. Maybe some dancin', too, if you're lucky." She stopped her fussing long enough to smile. "Jesse's a wonderful dancer."

"So?" Kate stood, pulling the panty hose up under her half slip to her waist, trying to pretend her pulse hadn't started racing just the tiniest bit at the thought of dancing with Jesse de Vallerin. He'd probably hold her far too close. His type always did. "What does dinner and dancing have to do with wearing panty hose?"

"You'll probably end up eatin' dinner on the balcony at Embers or on a patio somewhere in the Quarter, *without* air conditionin', that's what it has to do with it. And Jesse's as likely to take to dancin' in the street as anywhere else, anyway."

Dancing in the street, indeed, Kate thought. No Hightower had ever done such a thing. She dismissed the little voice that suggested it might be fun. "I always wear panty hose," she said firmly, sounding ex-

actly like Great-Aunt Katherine at her most auto-
cratic.

Lilac knew from experience it was her that's-the-
end-of-the-discussion voice, but twelve years of
friendship demanded she give it one more try. "I still
say you're goin' to roast."

"And I appreciate your concern," Kate said, reaching for the tailored, oyster-white dress. She stepped
into it, pulling it up over her long legs and curved hips,
sliding her hands into the armholes, settling it
smoothly over her full breasts. She felt much more like
herself in the dress, despite her misgivings about the
new hairdo. More able to deal coolly and competently with whatever an evening spent with a man like
Jesse de Vallerin might bring. "Zip me up, would you,
please?" she asked, turning to present her back.

Lilac sighed and reached for the zipper. "Jesse's not
likely to be dressed for church," she warned.

4

LILAC WAS RIGHT. Jesse wasn't dressed for church. He showed up at the door of Lilac's apartment promptly at seven-thirty, dressed in a crisp, pastel blue pin-striped shirt with no tie, a pale pink linen jacket and soft, faded jeans that were nearly as tight as the ones Kate had imagined him in the first time she saw him. Blindingly white sneakers, worn without socks, covered his feet. The tiny diamond stud glittered in his left ear. He looked fresh and cool and good enough to eat with a spoon.

Kate immediately felt overdressed and prim in her jacketed dress and panty hose and sensible beige pumps. She tightened her grip on her small, natural-straw clutch and tried to cover up her discomfort by bustling. "Well, I'd guess we'd better be going," she said, bending slightly to touch her cheek to Lilac's. "We'll be back by—" she hazarded a glance at her escort where he stood—*lounged* was a better word—against the door jamb "—what? Ten o'clock or so?"

Jesse's voice was slow and honey sweet, like his smile. "Wouldn't count on it," he warned, looking at her out of lazy blue eyes. "Things don't really get started in the Quarter until late, even on a Friday night." His gaze shifted to Lilac. "You just expect us when you see us, okay, darlin'?"

"Okay by me," Lilac said, waving them out the door. "Have fun, kiddies."

The door all but slammed, leaving them standing together on the small, sheltered porch above what had once been the stables of the large plantation-style mansion but now housed Lilac's landlord's three cars. Kate cleared her throat uncomfortably. "Well, I, uh . . ." Her gaze lifted to Jesse's, then shifted quickly away.

He was far too close. Much closer than she liked a man she barely knew to stand. Much closer than she liked *anyone* to stand. If she'd been wearing the eyelet halter dress, he'd have been staring down her cleavage. Just the thought made her nervous.

She fingered the narrow decorative cord on the rounded collar of her jacket. "I guess we'd better be on our way," she said again, edging away from him. Her hips came up against the wooden railing.

"I guess we should," he agreed, making no move to do so as he stood there, smiling at her with a look of seductive speculation in his blue eyes.

Kate squared her shoulders. "Well?" she demanded, sounding as imperious as a titled lady who'd been annoyed just once too often by an impudent footman.

Jesse's smile widened by one slow degree. "After you, darlin'," he said, turning so she could precede him down the narrow staircase. He ambled down the steps behind her, his sneakered feet making no sound on the wooden treads, his eyes on the brisk, no-nonsense shift of her hips under the oyster-white dress.

Luscious figure, he thought, viewing her with the eye of a true connoisseur. *Holds herself like somebody's maiden aunt, though. Somebody's Baptist missionary maiden aunt,* he amended. It'd be fun seeing if he could loosen her up a little. That's why he'd asked her out, he told himself. To loosen her up a little. It was a crime against nature for such a beautiful woman to hold herself on such a tight rein. And it was his duty, as a man who appreciated women, to help her relax.

Liar, he thought then, his smile turning wry and self-deprecating.

Asking her out had nothing to do with duty and everything to do with the steadily growing need to find out if her courtesan's mouth tasted as deliciously sinful as it looked. Sometime during the afternoon he'd just spent with his hands in her hair on a professional basis, he'd begun to wonder if she'd unbend enough to let him touch it on an unprofessional basis. And then, covertly watching Didi do her manicure while he'd pretended to be interested in the details of Miz Barclay's latest problems with her household staff, he'd found himself fantasizing those slim, patrician hands caressing his naked back while the ceil-

ing fan over his bed cooled their heated, passion-
flushed bodies.

And that—the mere possibility of *that*—was why
he'd asked her out. Altruism hadn't had anything at
all to do with it, except for the fact that he knew she'd
enjoy it, too, if she gave him a chance to show her how
it should be done.

Will you listen to yourself, de Vallerin? he chided
mentally. *You sound like the worse kind of male
chauvinist pig.*

But it was true. At least, it could be true. If she was
even half as attracted to him as he was to her, they
could both have a real good time. Whatever they
ended up doing.

She reached the crushed white rock driveway while
he was still only three-quarters of the way down the
stairs, still contemplating the pleasures they might
share. He could see the effort it cost her not to turn
around and tell him not to dawdle. He hurried his step
a little. Not much—it was too hot and humid to move
too fast—but enough to bring him into step beside her
as she moved down the driveway to the street.

"You've got to watch yourself on his gravel, darlin'," he said, cupping her elbow in his palm. It served
to support her steps and slow her down a bit. "You
could turn your ankle in those heels." He cast an appreciative glance down her legs. "And they're such
pretty ankles."

"The heels aren't that high," Kate said, but she didn't pull away. She told herself it was only good manners not to. He was, after all, only doing the gentlemanly thing. And then he slid his hand down her forearm and laced his fingers with hers. The warmth of his palm sent a jolt up her arm.

They both felt it.

Kate stiffened, pretending she hadn't.

Jesse smiled, pleased by her inadvertent, instinctive response. "This way," he said, tightening his fingers in an instinctive response of his own. "We catch the St. Charles streetcar right down there at the corner."

Streetcar? Kate thought, automatically following where he led. *Doesn't he have a car?*

"You mentioned this afternoon that you've never been to the Big Easy before," Jesse said, just as the streetcar tumbled to a stop in front of them. The Big Easy was New Orleans's nickname for itself, like Bean Town was for Boston, or the Big Apple for New York. "So I thought we'd just kind of wander around the Quarter for awhile," he said, gallantly assisting her as she stepped into the streetcar. He let go of her elbow to pay their fares. "Evenin', Leroy." He smiled his slow smile at the conductor. "Hot enough for you?"

The man chuckled, making some reply about it's never being hot enough for him, and then Kate felt Jesse's hand at the small of her back, guiding her down the narrow aisle.

She tried to stiffen her spine.

"After you've had a chance to soak up some of the atmosphere," he said from just behind her, "we'll decide where to eat." He stopped her with a light touch on the shoulder, silently inviting her take a seat, then folded himself down beside her. She scooted as close to the window as she could but they were still touching at the shoulder and hip and thigh. "How does that sound to you?" he asked.

"It sounds fine," Kate murmured, carefully inching her knee away from his.

It sounded awful but what else could she say? Good manners dictated that she agree to her escort's itinerary for the evening, even if he didn't seem to have one. Who, besides an irresponsible teenager, she asked herself, took a woman out without knowing where they were going?

Men who wore earrings, she answered herself. *Men who made a pale pink blazer look as dangerous and macho as a black leather motorcycle jacket. Men who moved as if they had oiled ball bearings for joints. Men who, furthermore, she had no business being out with in the first place, that's who!*

She sighed deeply, knowing it was too late to back out now.

"That's it, darlin'," Jesse said approvingly. "Just take yourself another deep breath of that New Orleans air," he advised, knowing full well she hadn't been savoring the air. "That sweet scent you smell is jasmine and honeysuckle and just a touch of Southern romance." He reached for her hand as he spoke and turned it palm up in his. "Heady as the perfume on a lady's wrist," he said, bending his head.

Kate felt his warm breath feather over the inside of her wrist. She went stock-still, every shred of common sense she possessed screaming at her to pull her hand away. Something stronger and more elemental tempted her to wait and see what he'd do if she didn't. "I don't wear perfume," she said primly, as a sop to her common sense, but her hand lay lax in his.

"No?" He inhaled again. "I could swear I smell lilacs." He looked up at her from under his lashes, his tawny blond head still bent over her hand, his seductive blue eyes full of merriment. "Have you been sneaking Lilac's bath oil?" he teased.

Kate nodded, unable to speak with him looking at her like that.

"Thought so. It smells different on you, though." He inhaled again, more deeply, closing his eyes as if to help him identify the scent. "More—" another slow inhalation, like an epicure savoring the bouquet of a fine wine prior to tasting it "—mysterious and—" he looked up quickly, catching her wide, fascinated gaze "—intensely female," he said, smiling appreciatively.

Kate stared for a second or two, as mesmerized as a child at her first magic show, before finally summoning up the will to wriggle her hand out of his grasp. "It's just plain old lilac," she said repressively.

Encroaching, presumptuous man, she thought, trying to tell herself she wished he'd keep his hands and his . . . his *observations* to himself.

It was vain and stupid, she scolded herself, to feel so ridiculously flattered at being called mysterious and intensely female by a man who probably said the same thing to every woman who came within touching distance. But she couldn't help it. She did feel flattered. Flattered and pleased and just a little bit excited. All right, very excited. No one had ever called her mysterious before. No one had ever told her she was intensely female.

Once, in the throes of passion, Reed had said she was beautiful but most of the time she had to be content with being merely attractive in her fiancé's eyes. Ex-fiancé's eyes, she reminded herself, stealing a quick, sideways glance at her companion.

What would Jesse say to a woman while in the throes of passion?

The thought jumped at her out of nowhere, bringing a rush of color to her cheeks. She shifted in her seat, turning toward the window in an effort to hide the blush that rose from the collar of her dress.

Now, what deliciously risqué little thought caused that? Jesse wondered, watching the quick color come and go in Kate's averted face. He knew it had to have been a risqué thought. Or one *she* thought was risqué.

Growing up with three sisters had taught him early that when a woman blushed like that it was usually over something she'd been taught was off limits for a lady to even think about. A woman as tightly strung as the one sitting next to him had probably been taught that lots of things were off limits. Lots of totally harmless, mutually pleasant, perfectly normal things. Someone should tell her that errant thoughts about sex were perfectly normal, he thought, leaning closer to put his lips next to her ear.

"This is New Orleans's business district," he said, restraining his baser impulses for the time being. "That's Lafayette Square. It's the second oldest square in New Orleans, Jackson Square in the Quarter being the oldest," he informed her.

She could smell the fresh mint scent of toothpaste and the more subtle fragrance of his after-shave. It was appealingly light and citrusy with a faint, heady hint of skin-warmed spice. She tried not to breathe too deeply.

"All those buildings around it are federal government offices. That one there is Gallier Hall. And over there—" he leaned across to point "—is the Chamber of Commerce." He sat back in his seat, inadvertently brushing the back of his arm against her breasts as he did so.

Kate felt her breath catch, deep in her chest. And then it rushed out again, leaving her breasts tingling with sensation. She lifted both hands in a quick, protective gesture, tugging the edges of her jacket closer together. The movement brought her forearms across her torso, and she pressed them against her breasts, unconsciously seeking to soothe the suddenly sensitive tips.

Jesse's lean, relaxed body tightened in immediate, equally unexpected sensual response. He touched the tingling flesh on the back of his arm and, very casually, crossed an ankle over the opposite knee, amazed at the strength of his response to an accidental touch. It made him wonder what would happen when they touched on purpose.

"As soon as we—" He cleared his throat, forcing his gaze away from the sight of her forearms pressing against the well-filled front of her dress and back to the view outside the streetcar window. "As soon as we cross Canal Street we'll be in the Vieux Carré." He pronounced it *view cah-ray*. "That's the French Quarter to you, darlin'," he said huskily, his gaze shifting, oh so casually, back to the bodice of her dress.

She'd lowered her hands to her lap. They were folded primly on top of her straw purse, proper as a nun in church. Her boxy little jacket hung exactly as its designer had intended it to, hiding all but the suggestion of her lush curves. Her eyes were glued to the passing scenery. "And that?" she asked, valiantly ignoring the slight blush that still warmed her cheeks. "What building is that?"

Jesse sighed, then, like the gentleman he was, resumed his soft-voiced travelogue, letting her pretend nothing had happened.

The streetcar turned onto Canal Street a moment later, clanking to a halt as the conductor called out the name.

"This is where we get off," Jesse said, getting to his feet before the car had come to a complete stop.

He took her hand as he rose, leading her down the aisle of the streetcar at a slightly faster pace than she'd seen him move before. He descended to the street ahead of her, turning to assist her down, and then waved a farewell to the conductor as the streetcar started back the way it had come.

"Canal Street is an unofficial boundary line of sorts," he said, leading her across the thoroughfare. "This is where the street names change and the business district gives way to the French Quarter." He stopped under a sign that announced the street name in both English and French. "This is where the aloof Creole culture of the Vieux Carré came up against the brashness of the Americans—the 'Kaintocks' they were called then—in 1803 when President Jefferson bought the Louisiana Territory for fifteen million dollars from Napoleon."

He lifted his free hand in a lazy arc that encompassed everything around them—the sights, the smells, the sounds—as if it was his own personal domain. "This, darlin'," he said, as if presenting it for her delectation, "is what New Orleans is all about."

Kate stood there on the street corner, drinking in the bustling street scene, with her hand warm in his and her breath coming just a bit too fast. She recognized a strange excitement in herself. A growing sense of anticipation. A sudden eagerness for . . . something. It wasn't a familiar feeling but it was one she wanted— needed—to explore further. "All about?" she murmured, lifting her gaze to him.

"It's a feast for the soul, darlin'." His eyes held hers as he spoke—teasing, effortlessly sensual blue gazing into expectant, curiously innocent brown. "A little tawdry around the edges, maybe, but a rich feast all the same. The Quarter is hot music and hot food and hot times," he told her in his slow, intimate drawl. "It's the romance and tradition of the Old South, all mixed up with the excitement of a modern port city. It's laughter and love, passion and—" he lifted the hand he held, bringing it to his lips, and looked at her over the back of it.

Something earthy and exciting and full of possibility hovered in the air between them as they stared into each other's eyes for an aeon's long split second. It swirled around them in the humid warmth of the evening air; in the heady scents of sun-warmed flowers growing in balcony planter boxes and the tantalizing odors of seafood and cooking spices from the restaurant across the street; it floated past in the soft wail of the tenor sax that drifted out of a doorway somewhere, and the far-off call of a Mississippi tug from across the levee.

Sex? she wondered, vaguely disappointed. Was that what danced in his blue eyes and made her nerves sizzle under her skin—just plain old sex?

"Life," Jesse said, kissing her fingers before he tucked them into the crook of his arm and led her into the heart of his beloved Quarter.

5

THEIR FIRST COURSE that evening was snowballs, a popular New Orleans treat served from stands and pushcarts all over the city.

"You've got to have one," Jesse insisted when she protested faintly that eating dessert first would ruin her appetite for dinner. "It's not really a dessert," he assured her, halting beside a ribbon-festooned pushcart. "It's an aperitif." He looked at the elderly man behind the pushcart for confirmation. "Tell her it won't ruin her appetite, Earl."

"No, ma'am," the vendor said obediently, grinning at the two of them. "Not a bit. Heck, it ain't nuthin' but a little bit of ice and flavored sugar syrup, is all."

"See there, darlin'? Nothing but a little ice and syrup." He smiled at the old man. "Make her a real nice one, now, Earl. This is Miz Kate Hightower." He slipped an arm around her shoulders, giving her a little squeeze as he introduced her. "She's a Yankee from up Boston way, and we want her to like New Orleans."

"Pleased to meet you," Kate murmured in response to the old man's nod. Casually, pretending an interest in the finer points of snowball making, she eased out from under the unnerving warmth of Jesse's arm to watch Earl form a mound of shaved ice on a paper plate.

Jesse let her go without protest, engaged in replying to a pithy comment from the old man in what was obviously an ongoing discussion of city politics.

"You best watch out for this here boy," Earl said, looking at Kate from under the brim of his baseball cap as he poured sweetened syrup over the mound of ice. "He can sweet-talk the ladies into losin' their good sense as easy as he sweet-talks those politicians over at City Hall."

Jesse cuffed him lightly on the shoulder. "That's some advice coming from a man with—how many is it, Earl? Eleven kids?"

"Eleven kids, sixteen grandkids and three great-grandkids, last count."

Jesse shook his head as if he couldn't believe it. "That's some mighty powerful sweet-talkin'."

"A whole lot more 'an just sweet talk," the old man shot back. "So you best heed my warnin', Miz Kate—" he handed her the finished snowball "—and don't let this here boy talk you into misbehavin'."

Smiling, Kate promised she wouldn't. And then promptly wondered what would happen if she did.

Misbehavin'. It sounded so innocent, like little kids getting into mischief. But misbehavin' with Jesse . . . Ah, now, the pictures *that* conjured up weren't innocent at all. Kate pushed them to the back of her mind almost as soon as they formed. Sex wasn't what she was anticipating, she told herself. Whatever it was that had shivered between them back there on the street corner, an interesting evening was the only thing on her agenda—she looked up just then, catching Jesse's teasing, conspiratorial grin—and never mind whatever might be on his.

They ate the snowballs with pink plastic spoons as they strolled through the Quarter. "A lady never eats in the street," Kate heard the voice of Great-Aunt Katherine say tartly. But she ignored it, listening instead to Jesse's melodious drawl as he pointed out the sights and recounted the legends about some of the beautiful old buildings, and insisted she trade him a taste of her raspberry snowball for his mint.

Unused to sharing someone else's food—"If you want dessert, Kate," Reed would say, "then order it—" she nevertheless found herself obediently opening her mouth for the spoonful of mint snowball Jesse fed her. She offered him the last bite of hers in return, laughing self-consciously when his tongue snaked out to keep a drop of the soupy treat from dribbling down his chin onto the pale perfection of his pink blazer.

"I can see you never fed any babies," Jesse teased, taking her empty paper plate and plastic spoon to drop them into a trash can as they passed it.

Kate arched a skeptical eyebrow. "And you have?"

"Dozens of times," he said airily and reached for her hand again.

Kate let him have it without protest, her mind occupied with a picture of sensual, sexy Jesse de Vallerin spoon-feeding a baby.

"Do you like oysters?" he asked, recalling her attention.

Kate resolutely shoved the thought of Jesse and babies to the back of her mind. "Love them," she said.

They entered a small Chartres Street café called Cliff's, run by an immense, bald black man who looked as if he should be wearing a Saints' football jersey instead of a chef's apron. He would have been even more intimidating, Kate thought, except for the smile that split his face in response to Jesse's introduction.

"Pleased to meet you," he said, nodding at Kate over the glass partition that protected the contents of his hot table. His smile turned into a sly grin as he looked at Jesse. "Where've you been hidin' yourself, man?" he asked, rubbing a huge hand over his shining pate. "I been wantin' to talk to you about that perm you gave me."

"Send Selima on over to my shop—" Jesse winked at Cliff's wife, on guard behind the cash register "—and I'll give her the same style, no charge."

The proprietor's only answer was a mock growl and a fancy move that sent his razor-honed chopping knife soaring end-over-end above his head before he snatched it out of the air.

"Clifford, you stop playing with those knives before you cut yourself, you hear?" Selima said, not even turning her head to make sure he did as he was told. "You should have some vegetables with that," she told Jesse as she handed him his change and the bag of food. "Fried food'll clog up your arteries without you have some vegetables with it."

"Always worrying about my health," Jesse said. He glanced at Kate. "Isn't she a darlin' to always be worrying about my health?" he asked, then turned back to Selima before Kate could answer, reaching around the cash register to squeeze her hand. "You ever get tired of that overgrown ox behind the counter," he said, loud enough for Cliff to hear, "you let me know."

Selima flipped her hand at him. "Oh, go on with you," she said as they exited the café.

They ate their take-out meal on a bench on the levee overlooking the Mississippi River, bathed in the long fingers of shadow and light cast by the lowering sun, talking about the things two people just getting to know each other talk about.

They discussed food.

"Should've warned you about the hot sauce," Jesse said, grinning as Kate gasped and reached for her iced tea. "It's Cliff's own special recipe. Here, let me get some of that off for you." He took her fried oyster sandwich, opening the two crusty halves of the po'boy loaf to dab at the hot sauce with a paper napkin. "That should do it," he said, handing it to her. He watched as she took a careful bite. "Better?"

Her mouth full, Kate could only nod.

They talked about the weather.

"I like the heat," Kate confessed, brushing at the bread crumbs in her lap with one hand while daintily holding her sandwich in the other. "It's always a relief when summer finally comes to Boston and I can pack the sweaters and mufflers away."

They talked about the only friend they had in common.

"Radcliffe had never seen anything like Lilac," Kate said.

And I've never seen anything like you, Jesse thought, fascinated by the contrast of her lush body and prim manner, and the way her soft courtesan's mouth shaped itself around her words.

"She'd bat her lashes in that wide-eyed way she has," Kate was saying, "and every man in sight was ready to slay dragons for—" she shifted into an approximation of Lilac's honeyed drawl "poor, helpless little ol' Lilac—" she resumed her more clipped Boston accent "—never suspecting that she could run rings around the best of them."

While you stood there like an imperious young queen, Jesse thought, *more than capable of slaying your own dragons, thank you very much, with no*

*idea at all of how tempting a challenge you were. And
are. Must have scared those college boys spitless.*

"It came in very handy when we wanted something moved," Kate said, her voice tinged with
amused admiration.

They talked about their families.

"Three sisters," Jesse said in answer to Kate's comment about being an only child. "Aimée, Ginny and
Chantal. With my mother being so young when she
started her family, though, most of the time it was like
having four." He smiled at the memories. "And I'm
here to tell you, being the only male in a houseful of
women can get pretty hectic at times—" he looked up
at her from under his lashes, his smile warm and teasing "—but it sure teaches you a lot about the so-called
weaker sex."

Kate made no comment to that. As far as she could
tell, Jesse de Vallerin was the kind of man who'd been
born knowing entirely too much about women. Having three sisters and an indulgent mother to round out
his education gave him an unfair superfluity of
knowledge.

They talked about their jobs.

"I administer the Hightower Charities," Kate told
him. "We award several scholarships every year and
set up grants for deserving projects that for some reason or other can't get government funding. Things like
that."

"Sounds like a high-powered job. I'm impressed."

"Well, don't be," Kate said, shaking her head. "Not with me, anyway. I don't actually have any direct responsibility for who gets the money. We have a board that does that. I just keep track of the details." She took another sip of her iced tea before putting it down on the bench between them. "Anybody could do it," she said, thinking of the Hightower women who'd held the position before her and the ones who would hold it after she'd gone on to something else.

"Still sounds interesting," Jesse insisted.

"Mmm," Kate said around a bite of her po'boy. "It is." Or, more accurately, it had been. She hadn't been getting a lot of satisfaction out of it for the past year or so. It was something else that was probably going to have to change, she thought dismally.

"How long are you on vacation?"

Kate lifted an eyebrow. "Vacation?"

"From your job."

"Oh, yes . . . vacation," she murmured, belatedly realizing that she was on a vacation. Sort of. "I've got the usual two weeks." Which she was supposed to be spending in Bermuda . . . on her honeymoon . . . with Reed. "So," she said brightly, suddenly desperate to change the subject, "what made you decide to become a hairstylist?"

"Just a natural-born talent for it, I guess," Jesse said. *Two weeks*, he was thinking. *Two weeks to teach the beauteous Miz Katherine Hightower to relax and have fun*. It didn't seem like enough time. "I've always been real good with my hands."

Yes, Kate thought, staring at him, *I'll just bet you have*.

He returned her stare, his brow lifted inquiringly.

Kate looked away, determined not to blush, and reached for her iced tea. The paper cup was empty.

"Here." Jesse reached out and took it from her. "Let me get rid of that for you. You finished with that, too?" he asked, indicating the remains of her oyster po'boy.

"Yes, thank you," she said politely, handing him the wrappings.

He dropped them in a trash bin and reached for her hand.

"We'll save dessert until later," he said as they passed the landmark open-air Café du Monde. "Beignets and chicory coffee are always best the very last thing before you call it a night." He gave her a teasing sideways glance. "Or the very first thing after you get out of bed in the morning."

Kate's only answer was a noncommittal murmur and a quick leap of her pulse at the mere thought of going anywhere near a bed with Jesse de Vallerin.

"Come on," he said, threading his fingers more tightly through hers. "Let's go listen to some jazz."

Kate had never been a fan of jazz—she'd never heard enough of it to decide whether it was something she might like—but she followed him willingly. They strolled through the darkening shadows in

Jackson Square, past St. Louis Cathedral, up the rue d'Orléans and onto Bourbon Street.

"Named for the French royal family," Jesse informed her. "Not the liquor."

It was full dark now but the street glowed with multicolored neon and the light pouring out of the open doorways of nightclubs and honky-tonks. Barkers offered glimpses into the striptease joints; music of all kinds filled the air; and there were people everywhere. They spilled off the narrow sidewalks onto the streets, a cheerful mass of boisterous, noisy humanity, bound and determined to have a good time, protected from traffic by the police barricades that blocked the roadway in both directions.

"Is there going to be a parade?" Kate asked.

Jesse shook his head. "The street is closed to traffic at night." He motioned toward the wooden barricades with his free hand. "Keeps people from getting mowed down by an irate driver."

"So they just get mowed down by each other," Kate said, edging closer to Jesse as they made their way down the crowded avenue. Someone bumped Kate from behind. She clutched her purse tighter with one hand and Jesse's hand tighter with the other. New experiences were one thing, but this cheerful, turbulent crowd was unsettling and just a bit too bizarre for her taste.

Jesse untangled his fingers from hers and draped his arm around her shoulders. "Better?"

"I—" Being so close to him exposed her to a different kind of experience, equally unsettling in its way but infinitely more welcome than the raucous, carefree crowd of people that flowed around them like eddies in a river. "Yes, much better," she said, reminding herself that he didn't mean anything by it. "Thank you."

Jesse smiled and tightened his arm, tucking her more securely under the curve of his shoulder. She fit just right against him, not so tiny that he had to stoop uncomfortably to hold her securely, nor so tall that he felt his protection was redundant. Her hand, riding hesitantly midway down his back as if she didn't quite know where to put it, spoke of a sweet shyness, excitingly at odds with the womanly warmth of her lush breast touching the side of his rib cage and the brush of her hip against his as they threaded their way through the crowd.

"We could go in here," he said, stopping in front of the open door of a jazz club. His smile was gently teasing. "Or if you want to walk and gawk some more, there's another club I can recommend a bit farther down the street."

Kate peered into the smoky interior of the club. Small, dim and crowded, it wasn't the kind of place she usually frequented, but then nothing about tonight was anything like what she usually did.

But wasn't that the real reason she'd agreed to go out with Jesse de Vallerin in the first place—and never

mind the odd, anticipatory way he made her feel—
because she was sick to death of what she usually did
and wanted a change? Well, tonight was certainly a
change and she was intent on experiencing it to the
fullest. She cast a quick, wary glance at the man beside her. Up to a point, anyway, she amended, shifting her gaze to the interior of the club.

It looked exactly as she'd always imagined a jazz
club would look. Not crowded, she decided, but intimate, with small round tables pushed close to each
other and the bandstand. Blue spots illuminated the
stage, cutting through the haze of smoke to cast their
moody glow over the trio of musicians and the black
woman in a slinky red dress singing something lan-
guorous about a love gone wrong.

"Let's go in," Kate said, ready for anything as she
walked out from under Jesse's arm to precede him into
the club.

Three different people called out greetings as they
threaded their way toward a free table. The singer
winked and wriggled the fingers of one hand. A mini-
skirted, flame-haired cocktail waitress hurried over
before they even had a chance to sit down.

"Jesse, honey." She threw one arm around his neck,
pulling herself up on tiptoe, and gave him a smacking
kiss on the lips. The tray of drinks balanced on the
palm of her hand didn't even wobble. The unbound
breasts beneath her black knit tank top did.

"Good to see you, too, Amber, darlin'," he said, returning her hug.

"Just wanted to say thanks again for last Saturday." She sank back on her heels and smiled up at him. "You were—" she broke off in response to an impatient call from another table. "Natives are thirsty tonight." She indicated the drinks on her tray with a quick tilt of her head that sent the ends of her long, red ponytail brushing over her shoulder. "Be back in a minute to take your order," she said, hurrying away as quickly as she'd come.

Kate watched her go, wondering if the waitress had even seen her, standing there beside "Jesse, honey." She sure hadn't acted like it.

Thanks for last Saturday? You were... Were what? Kate wondered, wishing the woman had stayed put long enough to finish the sentence.

Not that Kate couldn't make a pretty good guess. You were...great, awesome, incredible... Wasn't that the usual postmortem? Except in Jesse de Vallerin's case it was probably true, instead of being just polite fiction.

She glanced over her shoulder at him as he pushed her chair in for her.

He was incredibly handsome, of course, with those knowing blue eyes and that warm, golden skin and that teasing, lady-killer smile that quirked up his chiseled lips at the slightest provocation.

He was incredibly sexy, in a lazy, laid-back sort of way that made a woman wonder if he'd be as unhurried in his loving as he was with everything else.

And he was incredibly charming, too, if you went for that kind of outdated, exaggerated Southern chivalry, which, to her dismay, Kate found she did.

But would he really be all that incredible in bed?

Jesse gave her one of his slow, sweet smiles as he settled into the chair next to her and reached to take her hand with both of his. "What do you think?"

Only thirty years of ingrained good manners kept Kate's mouth from falling open in unladylike shock. "I beg your pardon?"

"What do you think?" Jesse repeated.

"I . . . ah . . ." Kate could feel the guilty color suffusing her cheeks and sent up a silent prayer that the club was too dark for him to notice. "About what?"

Jesse's eyes narrowed. *Was she blushing?* "About the club," he said, watching her over the hand he still held. *She was definitely blushing.* "The music."

"Oh. That." Relief flooded her, making her feel foolish for what she'd been thinking. "The music's very nice." She hadn't heard a note since the cocktail waitress had wrapped her lissome self around Jesse's neck. "And the club, well . . ." She tugged her hand out of his and waved it in front of her face. "It's a bit warm in here, don't you think?"

"A bit," he agreed. *Now what brought this on?* he wondered. Had she been thinking those risqué thoughts again?

He wasn't sure what had triggered them this time. The uncensored lyrics of the blues ballad the lady in red was singing? The couple at the next table with their tongues down each other's throats? The kiss he'd shared with Amber?

"Amber should be back in just a minute to take our drink order," he said to test his theory. "Something cold and wet should help cool you off."

"Yes." Kate picked up her straw clutch and began waving it in front of her face like a fan. "It should." *But I don't think it will.*

Jesse grinned like a fox who'd just figured out a foolproof way into the henhouse. If seeing him kiss Amber had gotten the prim little Miz Hightower this hot and bothered, what was she going to do when he kissed her?

And he was going to kiss her. Soon. And it wouldn't be an affectionate little peck like he'd given Amber, either, but a long, thorough, tongue-tasting kiss that was going to leave both of them hot and bothered. What happened after that would be up to her, of course, but he would do his best to convince her that whatever happened should happen in his bed. Tonight.

"Sorry I took so long." The cocktail waitress reappeared at their table as if she'd materialized out of the smoky air. "You gonna have your usual, Jesse?"

Of course, she'd know his "usual," Kate thought sourly, and then was thoroughly annoyed at herself for feeling that way. She had no reason to be upset because some redheaded cocktail waitress with perfect little breasts and absolutely no hips at all knew Jesse's preferences in alcohol. *And probably everything else, too*, she thought, feeling herself flush again as her wayward mind obediently began conjuring up explicit images of exactly what that "everything else" included.

"B and B'll be fine." Jesse confirmed his drink order without taking his gaze from Kate's flushed face. "What would you like, darlin'?" he asked softly, his tone as intimate as if they were already in bed.

You, she thought, before she could stop herself. She fanned faster. "I'll have a martini," she said, naming the first drink that popped into her head. "No, wait—" there was a slightly panicky edge to her voice "—not a martini."

Martinis were what had gotten her into this in the first place!

"Kate, darlin'." Jesse reached out and captured her wrist, stopping her frantic fanning. "Tell Amber what you'd like to drink."

"Ah . . . gin and tonic. Light on the gin," she added, just to be on the safe side. As if alcohol was the real problem! She stood suddenly, her straw purse clutched to her midsection like a shield. "Is there a ladies' room in here?"

"Back past the end of the bar." Amber gestured with one hand. "First door on the left," she added, but Kate was already weaving her way through the closely-packed tables. Amber looked at Jesse. "She okay?"

"She's fine," he drawled, his blue eyes smoldering with a sensual heat as they followed the rapidly retreating figure of his date. "Real fine."

Kate all but slammed the door to the tiny bathroom, then leaned against it, breathing as if she'd just run a footrace with the devil.

Which, she thought, wasn't all that far from the truth.

Jesse de Vallerin was a devil, all right. A teasing, tempting, slow-moving, sweet-talking Southern devil.

"How did I get myself into this?" she whispered.

All she'd wanted was a change. Just a little something different to add some excitement to the increasingly humdrum routine of her well-ordered life.

Well, Jesse de Vallerin was something different, all right. Different enough, in fact, to excite her right out of the good sense she'd been born with. And probably right out of a lot of other things, too, if she wasn't careful—like her clothes. The very thought made her pulse race and her breath come too fast.

"Take a deep breath," she told herself, unconsciously using the very same words her great aunt had always used to put things in perspective for a much younger Kate, "and calm down. Getting into a tizzy never solved anything."

Kate took a deep, slow breath, and then another one, all the while staring at herself in the mirror as if she were staring at a stranger. Her face was rosy with emotion and heat. Her eyes were wide and round and vaguely unfocused, as if she had just awakened from a dream. Her newly layered hair had gained volume in the humidity, gleaming a definite red where the overhead light hit it, tumbling to her shoulders in little renegade curls and tendrils. A fitting metaphor, she thought, for the sudden twists her life had taken since yesterday. She ruthlessly smoothed her palms down the length of her unruly hair. The motion didn't do anything but remind her of how much better Jesse's hands had felt doing the same thing.

"Oh—" an appropriate swear word wasn't immediately forthcoming "—hell. Hell. Hell," she said forcefully, in direct violation of Great-Aunt Katherine's edict that a well-educated person need never resort to vulgar profanity in order to make a point, which probably just proved, Kate thought spitefully, that her great-aunt had never been tempted by a sensual blue-eyed devil.

Resolutely she turned on the cold water tap, holding each wrist in turn under the flow of water before moistening a paper towel to cool her face and throat. Then, staring herself straight in the eyes, she took another deep breath, tossed her hair and squared her shoulders. Opening the bathroom door, she stepped into the smoky club, determined to resist temptation to her last breath.

JESSE WAS JUST ABOUT TO GET UP and go see if anything was wrong when Kate appeared around the end of the bar. He stood as she approached and held her chair for her, tucking it in under her legs as she sat.

"I hope your drink's light enough on the gin," he said, nodding toward the tall, frosty glass in front of her as he seated himself.

Kate picked it up and sipped without looking at him. "Yes, it's fine, thank you," she said, putting it down.

"I can order you something else if you'd rather."

"No." Kate ran her finger up and down the side of the glass and avoided looking at him. "This is fine."

"Would you rather have a cup of coffee?" Jesse offered, his eyes on her moving fingers. He imagined them on his skin, cool and moist from the glass, warming as they absorbed his heat. "Or an iced tea?"

"No." The word came out more sharply than Kate had intended, all out of proportion to his simple inquiry. "That is—" She lifted her gaze briefly, catching his, then just as quickly lowered it. He was looking at her like *that* again. She could almost feel her spine softening. Temptation, she thought, was a lot harder to resist when you were staring right at it! "Actually," she began, "what I'd really like is a couple of aspirin." She pressed two fingers to the middle of her forehead. "My head..." She let her voice trail off, hoping she wasn't overdoing it.

Jesse leaned forward, reaching out to lay a hand on her forearm. "You don't feel well?"

"I think the smoke—"

He was on his feet before she could finish the lie, already reaching into his back pocket for his wallet. "You should have said something sooner," he admonished gently.

He dropped a few bills on the table, then stuffed the billfold into his jeans pocket with one hand while reaching to cup her elbow with the other. "Let's get you out into the fresh air, darlin'," he said, lifting her out of her chair as gently as if she were made of spun glass. "Don't forget your purse." He handed it to her. "We'll see if we can get you some aspirin on the way out, okay?" he said, as he led her between the tables.

Kate could only nod dumbly, amazed at how quickly his expression had gone from lazy sensuality to warm concern. "Kate isn't feeling well," Jesse said to Amber as she hurried up to them with a questioning frown between her brows.

"Oh, dear," the cocktail waitress said sympathetically. "I thought something was the matter when you went dashing off to the bathroom like that. Upset stomach?" she asked Kate.

Jesse looked at his date as if he'd just realized the possible significance of her flushed face and the frantic trip to the bathroom. "Bad oysters?"

"No. No, of course not," Kate hastened to reassure them both. "It's just a headache," she said, feeling more deceitful every minute. "Really. I just need to get some fresh air and clear my head."

"And we're standing here, talking you to death," Jesse said. He shifted his hand from her elbow to curl it around her shoulders. "Would you see if Mark has some aspirin behind the bar?" he said to Amber as he led Kate away. "We'll be over by the door."

Amber brought her a glass of water with the unneeded aspirin, standing by to take the glass when Kate had finished with it.

"You take care of yourself, now, you hear?" Amber said, after Kate had handed her the empty glass. "And come on back and see us again when you're feeling better."

Kate nodded. "Yes, of course," she said pleasantly, feeling as if she might really have a headache coming on after all.

After flashing Amber a quick smile, Jesse silently led Kate outside and through the throng on Bourbon Street to a less busy side street. In minutes, they were walking through a much quieter, more peaceful part of the French Quarter.

Jesse brought their progress to a halt under a street-light. "Feeling any better?" he asked, releasing her to dig two fingers into the front pocket of his jeans.

Kate shrugged, perversely missing his arm around her, and averted her eyes from the way his jeans pulled across his groin.

"Well, you'll feel better as soon as you're tucked into bed," he said, smiling as he held up the key he'd extracted from his pocket.

Kate's gaze snapped to him, unable to believe what she'd heard. *As soon as you're tucked into bed!* Just what did he mean by that, she wondered, afraid she already knew. *His* bed, was what he meant.

Jesse wasn't looking at her and so missed her deepening frown. He'd turned toward the decorative wrought-iron gate that guarded the darkened arcade-type alley next to what she suddenly realized was the front door of Images. "I live over my shop," he said as he fit the key into the lock.

Why am I surprised? Kate thought, staring at his back as he jiggled the key in the lock. It was what she should have expected—exactly what she had been expecting—from a man like him. He'd brought her to his place and now he thought he was going to seduce her. And without even bothering to lead up to it by offering her a cup of coffee first! Well, he could just think again, she fumed. She wasn't some weak-willed, bubble-brained female who fell into bed just because some good-looking—all right, *gorgeous*—stud smiled at her.

No manner how tempting.

Not even when, for the first time in her life, it was very, very tempting.

Jesse pushed the gate open, standing back to allow her to precede him into the covered alley. "There's a courtyard in back where—" She stood there, staring at him with a look on her face that reminded him of the way Sister Madeline had looked at him the time she'd caught him hiding a girlie magazine inside his catechism text when he was in the sixth grade—disappointed, angry and judgmental all at once. He tried to ignore the automatic spurt of guilt. "Kate?"

"I'd rather just go on back to Lilac's."

"Of course you would," he agreed, used to dealing with women made pettish by minor illness. He held out his hand, smiling at her encouragingly. "But you come on in first while I—"

"I'd really rather just go on back to Lilac's," she repeated, standing her ground. "Now," she added and crossed her arms under her breasts.

Jesse continued smiling at her, his hand held out, for another second or two and then, quite suddenly, her meaning got through to him. *She thinks I brought her here to make a move on her,* he thought, incredulous and more than a little insulted.

Never mind that what she was thinking had been true thirty minutes ago. It most certainly wasn't true now. He didn't make passes at women who weren't feeling well. It was inconsiderate and ungentlemanly and just plain crude. He dropped his hand. No woman had ever intimated, not by so much as the flicker of an eyelash, that he was crude. And here she was, with her luscious mouth screwed up as if she'd just bitten into a lemon, staring at him as if he were some kind of pervert. He didn't like it one little bit.

"My car keys are in my apartment," he said coolly. "You can wait here on the street or come on in to the courtyard while I run up and get them. Your choice." He disappeared into the sheltered colonnade without another word.

Kate hesitated, confused by the hint of indignation in his voice, and then, after glancing uneasily down the nearly empty street, followed him into the darkness. He was already making his way up the wooden stairs to his apartment when she emerged into the courtyard.

Like so many New Orleans courtyards, it was paved with weathered brick, lush with fragrant flowers, alive with the tinkling sound of the stone fountain in its center. Soft, golden light from a lantern-shaped fixture at the base of the staircase enabled Kate to make out the outlines of the fountain and flowerpots and the white wrought-iron chairs and table partially hidden in the shadow of the gallery formed by the upstairs porch. She sank down into one of the chairs, wondering if, just possibly, she'd been wrong.

Maybe he hadn't brought her here to seduce her, after all.

She felt a sharp stab of disappointment at the thought and hurriedly tamped it down. It was all good and well he didn't intend to seduce her, she told herself, because she didn't intend to allow herself to be seduced. Still, it wasn't very flattering to think he wasn't even going to try.

"Lord, will you listen to yourself?" she whispered into the darkness. Running out of the church had obviously affected more than just her wedding plans; it had addled her heretofore perfectly fine thought processes and turned her brain to warm mush. She sighed and closed her eyes, leaning her head back on the edge of the wrought-iron chair.

Standing on the porch above her, Jesse felt all his indignation melt away. She looked so defenceless, so utterly, deliciously feminine, sitting there in the chair below him with her head thrown back in an attitude of utter exhaustion and her eyes closed. Light from the lantern spilled over her left shoulder, highlighting the perfection of her luscious lips and the soft rise and fall her breast and the pale elegance of her hand where it lay on the arm on the chair.

He made his silent, lightfooted way down the steps and put his hand on her shoulder. "Kate?"

She gave a muffled squeak, jerking upright as if he'd scalded her.

"Hey, take it easy, darlin'." He gave her an easy grin and backed off, holding his hands up, palms out, as if to show her he intended no harm. "Ready to go?"

"Go?"

"Back to Lilac's." He moved toward a large pair of doors set into the wall next to the covered alley as he spoke. "You'll feel better after a good night's sleep." Pulling one of the doors open, he reached in and flicked on a light, illuminating a vintage 1966 electric blue Mustang convertible in showroom condition.

So he has a car after all, Kate thought as Jesse moved to put up the white fabric top.

"No," she said, coming up behind him. "Leave it down." She hadn't ridden in a convertible in years, not since her college days, at least. She wondered why that was; she'd always loved the feel of the wind in her hair.

"You're sure?"

"Positive. It'll help blow the cobwebs out of my head."

She was right. By the time Jesse came to a stop on the white gravel dirt beneath Lilac's apartment, she was feeling no trace of a headache, either real or imagined.

"That was lovely," she sighed, completely forgetting to be on her guard. She rolled her head against the back of the seat, turning to look at him. "Cleared my head right up," she said, smiling. "Thank you, Jesse."

"My pleasure." He turned toward her to rest his arm along back of her seat. There was a very purposeful look in his blue eyes.

Kate straightened and put her hand on the door handle. "No need to see me up," she said brightly, suddenly remembering why she'd pretended to have a headache in the first place.

He was right behind her as she made her way up the narrow staircase. She fumbled with the key Lilac had given her until Jesse put his hands on her shoulders and turned her to face him.

She stared at his chin. "I had a lovely time," she said, feeling absurdly like a high school girl on her first date. Except that she hadn't felt this awkward on her first date.

"So did I." He put his forefinger under her chin and lifted her head. Their eyes met. "Headache all gone?"

"Yes," she answered honestly and then, when she saw the flare of passionate intent in his eyes, "I mean . . . that is . . ."

His lady-killer grin flashed for just a moment. "Too late," he said and bent his head.

Kate stood very still, waiting for the first touch of his mouth on hers. It was everything she'd intuitively known it would be. Soft, delicate and experimental, the first testing kiss of an experienced man, sweetly seeking rather than demanding, a what-do-we-have-here sort of kiss that gently coaxed her to return it.

She sighed with pleasure.

Jesse realigned their lips to a more satisfying angle and took the kiss deeper, turning it hot and languid with the sliding invasion of his tongue and the tightening of his hands on her shoulders.

Kate melted into him, her head falling back, her body leaning into his, her nerve endings tingling and buzzing and clamoring for more. She had never been kissed so thoroughly, so voluptuously, with such single-minded attention. She felt as if she could have stood there, on Lilac's front porch, and kissed Jesse de Vallerin all night long.

But soon, too soon, he drew away. It was that, he thought, or yank her prim little dress up around her waist and her panty hose down past her knees and ravish her against Lilac's front door. "Will I see you again?" he said against her lips. His hands were still cupped around the delicate bones of her shoulders, holding her upright and himself under rigid control.

Kate swayed towards him. "Yes," she said. It would have taken a woman a lot stronger than she was to even think of saying no right then.

"Good." He kissed her once more, hard, as if he couldn't stop himself, and set her away from him. "I'll call you."

And then he was gone, moving lightly down the steps with his lazy, masculine grace. Kate stood where she was with Lilac's key clutched in her hand, watching as he got into his blue convertible and drove away, feeling as if she were going to slide down the front door to land in an ignominious heap of quivering feminine need on Lilac's bright blue welcome mat.

6

"HE HASN'T CALLED."

Lilac grinned at the wall she was painting a pale lavender. "Who?" she said, as if she didn't know.

Kate paused in midstroke to glare down at her deliberately obtuse best friend. "You know very well who," she said, stabbing her paintbrush into the open can of paint sitting below her on the ladder's pail rest.

Lilac kept right on painting; she wasn't going to be the first one to bring his name up. She'd done it yesterday afternoon around about the third time Kate had nearly jumped out of her skin at the sound of a ringing phone, and almost gotten her head taken off for her pains. If Kate wanted to talk about Jesse de Vallerin, she was going to have to introduce his name into the conversation herself.

Kate sighed loudly, like someone who'd been shamefully mistreated but wouldn't dream of mentioning it, and wielded the paint-loaded brush with more force than was strictly necessary.

Lilac moved out of the way of the splattering paint and didn't say a word.

"Jesse, that's who," Kate said into the silence.

"Oh." Lilac's grin got wider. "Him."

"Yes, him." She looked at the top of Lilac's blond head, fighting the unladylike urge to tip the can of paint on it. Why wasn't she offering advice and opinions? Kate wondered. Lilac was always full of advice and opinions when Kate didn't need them and now, when she needed them desperately, the other woman decided to practice discretion. "Why hasn't he called?" Kate demanded. She couldn't keep the question to herself any longer.

"I thought you didn't want him to. He isn't your type, remember?"

"That's not the point. He *said* he'd call," she complained. "I just like people to do what they say they're going to do."

"Why? So you can tell him to get lost?"

"Yes. No. Oh, hell." Kate stabbed her paintbrush into the can of paint again. "I don't know."

And the trouble was, she didn't. She had absolutely no idea what she'd say to him if he did call. Not a clue. It was almost scary. She, Katherine Victoria Frances Hightower, didn't know what to say to one man. A man, moreover, who wasn't even her type in the first place.

"Oh, who am I kidding?" she muttered. He was so much her type he made her palms sweat.

"I beg your pardon?" Lilac said politely.

"I wasn't talking to you," Kate snapped.

Lilac tsked and shook her head. "That's a bad sign, you know, honey. Talkin' to yourself. Usually means you've got it real bad."

Kate arched an eyebrow. "*It?*" she questioned imperiously.

"Man trouble."

"Oh, I do not!"

Lilac gave her a look.

"Okay," she admitted, applying paint very carefully to avoid meeting Lilac's knowing eyes, "maybe I do. A little," she qualified. "The question is . . ."

"Yes?" Lilac prompted sweetly. "The question is?"

"The question is . . ." Kate took a deep breath and decided to just go ahead and ask. Lilac already knew, anyway. "What do I do about it?"

It was exactly the opening Lilac had been waiting for. "Well, it's not what I'd do, of course, but you bein' a liberated Yankee and all, well—" she looked up, all innocence and earnestness "—you could try callin' him."

Kate gave up all pretense of painting. "And say what, exactly?"

Lilac put her paintbrush down, too. "I doubt you'd have to say much of anythin' after you said hello. Jesse's not stupid. He'll know what you want without you tellin' him."

She was almost afraid to ask. "Which is?"

Lilac's grin was pure mischief. "Why, for him to come on over here and kiss you silly again, that's what."

Kate could feel the heat rising to her cheeks. "Who says he kissed me silly?"

"Oh, come on, Kate. I'm not stupid. I saw that look on your face when you came floatin' into my apartment Friday night. It's the same one that's on your face right now, from just rememberin' it."

Kate didn't bother to deny it. Lilac, as usual, was right. After Jesse had kissed her good-night, she'd had barely enough wits left to get the front door unlocked.

"And after he kisses me silly again?" she demanded. "Then what?"

"You're a big girl. I'm sure you know what to do with a gorgeous hunk of man like Jesse. And if you don't, well, he—"

"But I shouldn't even be *interested* in a gorgeous hunk like Jesse," Kate said morosely. "That's the problem."

"Huh?"

"Lilac, think! Up until three days ago I was engaged to Reed."

"So? You're not engaged to him now."

"That's not the point. I *was* engaged. I was going to be married in— My God—" she turned around where she stood and plunked herself down on the third rung of the ladder "—I was going to be married today!" she said, amazed horror in her voice. "Tonight would have been my wedding night."

Lilac shuddered theatrically. "Kind of gives you the heebie-jeebies, doesn't it?"

Kate couldn't help it. She laughed. "Oh, Lilac, what am I going to do?"

"Well," she said, as if the question was one that demanded an answer, "you could start by takin' my advice."

"Oh, right! And get myself involved with a man just because I like the way he kisses."

"There are worse reasons."

"Maybe," Kate agreed, although privately she couldn't think what those reasons might be. "For some people. But I happen to think there should be more to a relationship than just the physical. You know, things like shared interests and common goals?"

"Like you had with Reed?"

Kate ignored her remark as unworthy of comment. "*If* I was interested in another relationship, I'd want it to have some . . . some weight to it. Some substance."

"Who says a relationship with Jesse would be insubstantial?"

"That's all it could be. I won't be down here long enough to build any kind of lasting relationship with him, even if I wanted to." *Which I don't.*

"Well, then, how about an insubstantial relationship?" Lilac suggested wickedly. "You know, a fling? Now, *that'd* be a real change for you."

THE PHONE RANG an hour later. Being the one with her feet on the ground, Lilac put her paintbrush down, wiped her hands on a rag and went to answer it.

"Secrets," she cooed seductively, trying out the name of her new store on the unsuspecting public for the first time. "Can I help you?"

There was a pause while whoever was on the other end of the line answered her question.

"Why, how nice to hear from you," Lilac said, shooting a smug, triumphant look at the woman on the ladder.

Kate was diligently applying herself to spreading the paint, pretending she wasn't straining her eardrums to listen to Lilac's half of the conversation, and didn't see her expression.

"Uh-huh," Lilac murmured into the telephone. "We've been paintin' since early this mornin'.... Well, lilac, of course." She laughed softly, flirtatiously. "What else would I use? Uh-huh. It's goin' to look real nice if I do say so myself."

There was a moment of silence while her caller spoke.

"A picnic? Yes, that sounds lovely. I'm sure she'd love it."

Kate glanced around at that, instinctively knowing the she in question was herself.

"No, she can't come to the phone right now but I know she'd love to." Lilac gave another low laugh. "Why, of course I'm sure."

"I'd love to what?" Kate asked, starting to back down the ladder.

"Because we were just talkin' about you, that's how I know," Lilac said into the telephone, "and she was sayin'—"

"Is that Jesse?" Kate demanded, knowing very well it was. Who else had they been talking about?

"No, on second thought, I don't think I'll tell you what she said," Lilac teased her caller. "I'll let her tell you. In twenty minutes? Yes, that'd be fine."

"In twenty minutes what?" Kate made a grab for the phone.

Lilac turned away, keeping it out of Kate's reach. "Yes, casual. Uh-huh, I'll tell her. 'Bye now." She cradled the receiver. "That was Jesse," she said. "He's picking you up in twenty minutes."

"I DON'T KNOW what you're so upset about, Kate." Lilac stood in the doorway of the tiny bathroom, watching Kate scrub at the pale lavender paint dabbling her hands. "He said it was casual."

"Casual is one thing." Kate plucked at the front of the faded football jersey she'd borrowed from Lilac. "Looking like a ragpicker is another."

"Better not let Jesse hear you say that. He has season tickets for the Saints."

Kate ignored her, turning instead to look at her rear view in the mirror. "I can't go anywhere looking like this," she wailed, tugging at the hem of the white drawstring shorts she'd also borrowed from Lilac. They'd been fashionably baggy on the smaller woman; they were unfashionably snug on Kate. She'd never in her life gone anywhere dressed in such a haphazard way.

"Pull the jersey down a little bit." Lilac reached out, suiting action to word. "See? Isn't that better?"

"Now it looks like I'm not wearing anything else."

"Well—" Lilac sighed in exasperation "—pull it up then. Here, let me fix it." She grabbed a handful of fabric at the hem and twisted it into a knot on Kate's hip. "There. Instant fashion."

Kate still looked dubious. "I don't know."

"Your only other choice is something from one of those boxes in the storeroom," she said, knowing it was no choice at all. The boxes in the storeroom were full of the very expensive lingerie Lilac meant to sell in Secrets when it opened.

"Cute," Kate said. "Very—"

The bell over the front door rang, signaling the entrance of someone.

Kate felt her heart all but stop. "Jesse," she breathed.

HE TOOK HER to Chalmette National Park, six miles outside the city, and spread a tan-and-blue plaid blanket on the grass beneath the sheltering branches of a centuries-old oak. They had the slow-moving Mississippi to look at while they ate and a plantation house turned park museum in the distance behind them.

"This is a wonderful spot for a picnic, Jesse. Just—" Kate took a deep breath of the warm, rich air, spreading her arms in an all-encompassing gesture "—*wonderful*." She looked at the man kneeling between the insulated cooler and the wicker basket they'd carried from the car. "Thank you for bringing me here."

Jesse looked up, a bottle of wine in one hand, and gave her one of his slow, sweet smiles. "You're more than welcome, darlin'," he said, then gestured toward the blanket. "Sit yourself down and relax." His smile turned wicked. "I don't bite."

I'll bet, Kate thought, stubbornly ignoring the heat that sizzled up her spine. She sank to her knees on the blanket and gestured toward the picnic basket. "Can I help?"

Jesse shook his head. "You're my guest. Here—" he handed her a tapered glass shimmering with golden wine "—prepare your palate for the best boiled shrimp in the entire South."

Kate took the wine and settled onto her hip with her bare legs tucked to one side, more than content to let Jesse play host. Watching him prepare their lunch, she wondered if she were crazy to feel so relaxed and so . . . so absurdly happy to be on a picnic with a man who wasn't even remotely her type when she should— on this very day!—have been exchanging wedding vows with a man everyone said was perfect for her?

She decided she didn't care. Not right now. Right now, all she cared about was spending the rest of the afternoon with Jesse de Vallerin, and to hell with the guilt she should be feeling for having jilted her fiancé practically at the altar.

"So," she said, determined to put aside everything but her enjoyment of the afternoon and the man she was spending it with. "Do you come here often?"

He looked up from the food he was fixing, his grin quick and teasing. "Lilac give you that line?"

Kate smiled and shook her head. "It isn't a line. I'd just like to know more—" *everything!* "—about you." She set her wine on the flat top of the picnic basket and reached for the plate he handed her. "After all, we seemed to talk mostly about me the other night."

"Okay." He set a basket of crusty French bread and a container of spicy Creole cocktail sauce within easy reach, then settled back, cross-legged, with his own plate of shrimp. "What deep dark secrets would you like me to reveal to you?"

"Oh, nothing that drastic. Just—" she pushed a shrimp around with the tines of her fork "—where did you go to school? Have you always wanted to be a hairstylist? Have you ever been married or—" she stuck her fork into a boiled shrimp "—engaged?" *And just what is Amber, the cocktail waitress, to you?* "All the normal getting-to-know-you kinds of questions."

"Well, let's see." Jesse dipped a shrimp into the cocktail sauce. "I graduated from high school right here in New Orleans. Went to cosmetology school here, too." No need, he thought, to mention that college had been out of the question because his family had needed the money he could earn working full-time. "As for always wanting to be a hairstylist, that was kind of a gradual thing. I mean, being surrounded by women all his life, a man tends to learn all about their hair and makeup and such without quite being aware he is learning."

He popped the sauce-coated shrimp into his mouth, chewing thoughtfully for a moment before he went on.

"Leastways, I think that's where the interest came from. Anyway, what with my sisters always asking their big brother's opinion about a new hairdo or lipstick or whatever—" he shrugged and dipped himself another shrimp "—it kind of grew from there. The first time I actually cut anyone's hair was when Chantal—she was fourteen, I think—and a friend gave each other these awful geometric haircuts they'd tried to copy out of some magazine. Poor Chantal was frantic." He shook his head, smiling at the memory. "She begged me to do something before Mama came home and saw what she'd done to herself. The next day at school, everyone was asking where she'd gotten her hair done and before I knew it, all her friends were asking me to cut their hair, too."

"Lilac said you used to do hers before a big date."

Jesse nodded. "Hers and about a dozen other girls'. And I'm here to tell you, it didn't do too much for my macho image with the other guys at school—" he grinned in that sweetly wicked way of his "—until I pointed out that I'd run my fingers through the hair of some of the most popular girls in the entire school. A few of the guys started reading hairdo magazines after that," he said, deadpan.

Kate laughed, as she was meant to. "Did it do them any good?"

"What?" Jesse said, his eyes on her lips as they formed a smile. "The magazines?"

Kate nodded.

Jesse shook his head. "The jocks were all thumbs and most of the others were too shy to talk to a girl, let alone get close enough to fix her hair."

"A malady you've never suffered from, I'll bet," Kate said.

"Not even a glimmer," Jesse agreed. He set his plate aside and picked up his half-full glass of wine. "So—" he took a deep, appreciative sip "—what were the other questions? Oh, yes, I remember," he said before Kate could answer. "Have I ever been married or engaged." He drained his wineglass and set it on his empty plate. "No, I haven't," he said, looking into her eyes across the three feet of plaid blanket that separated them. "Have you?"

Kate didn't quite know what to say to that. "I was engaged. Once," she said finally, making it sound as if it had been a long time ago. It suddenly felt as if it had been a long time ago. Ages ago. Another lifetime ago.

Jesse held her eyes, a searching look in his. "Are you still in love with him?"

"No." She felt guilty about that, guilty enough to make her sound a little bit hesitant.

"You sure?"

"Yes," she said firmly. "Absolutely positive."

"Good." He leaned over, pushing her empty plate out of the way, and plucked her wineglass from her hand to set it out of harm's way. And then, gently, inexorably, he pressed her back onto the picnic blanket. "I've been dying to kiss you again," he said and covered her tempting courtesan's mouth with his.

Well, finally, she thought, sinking back onto the blanket without a whimper of protest.

Just like two nights before, Kate sighed at the first touch of his mouth on hers. And, just like before, the kiss turned deep and languid and hot. But, unlike the time before, it didn't stop there.

There was a soft moan and a murmur and a subtle rolling shift of bodies that brought him on top of her; an unconscious flexing of a bare knee that settled his jeans-clad leg between hers and brought his hand sliding up the satin flesh of her thigh. His long fingers burrowed under the edge of her shorts at the back of her leg. Her hands kneaded the firm, resilient muscle beneath the fabric of his soft white shirt. And then, as naturally as breathing, she tilted her hips upward in the age-old gesture of feminine need and he answered with the thrust and grind of masculine aggression that showed her how near the edge they were.

Kate moaned and stiffened beneath him, suddenly aware of where she was and what she was doing and who she was doing it with. "Jesse." She tugged at the handful of shirt in her curled fingers. "Jesse, stop. I can't do this!" she said a bit frantically.

His hand tightened on the curve of her buttock for just a moment, holding her as if he wouldn't let her resist, and then his fingers relaxed and fell to the blanket. He tore his mouth from hers and buried his face in the tumbled auburn hair at her neck. They were both breathing hard, hearts pounding, bodies pulsing and throbbing in deep secret places, unconsciously pressing those places together despite their awareness they must stop.

"A minute," he murmured into her hair. "Just give me a minute."

She nodded against his cheek, needing the minute as badly as he did.

Slowly, gradually, taking several times more than a minute, their breathing became a little easier and their hearts stopped trying to beat out of their chests and their bodies eased apart. Not far apart, but far enough to bring a tiny measure of sanity to them both.

As he drew away from her that little bit, easing his weight to the side, Kate felt embarrassment come rushing in. She'd never lost control before. She'd thought she had, once or twice, but she'd been wrong. Even in her most intimate, intense encounters with Reed she'd still retained a sense of herself and what she was doing. But this . . . this was like catching fire and not being able, not wanting, to put it out. Like going crazy and not caring. Like—

"I don't know what came over me," she said, appalled and thrilled and frightened all at once.

"It's just healthy, yearning female hormones, darlin'," Jesse said raggedly, still struggling to control his ragingly healthy hormones. "Just nature, doing her best to get us together," he added, wondering if that's really all it was. He wanted her, certainly; he'd known that about ten minutes after he'd laid eyes on her. But simple lust had never taken him so deep, so fast, so furiously before. It was kind of scary—in a strangely wonderful sort of way—to realize he actually ached with wanting her.

He'd never ached before. Not like this. Not even when he was seventeen and dying over the refusal of his high school sweetheart to let him touch her under her clothes.

He wanted to touch Kate under her clothes, he realized. Right now, this minute, and damn the fact they were lying on a blanket by the riverbank in full view of anyone who might happen by, and that she'd already signaled her unwillingness to go further. She was still half under him, yielding and sweet, and he wanted, desperately to touch her breasts and her belly and the soft, warm place between her thighs that had been pressing so sweetly against his leg just a moment ago. He bent his head again, seeking her mouth, and ran his hand up her rib cage, intent on fulfilling his desire.

She turned her face away and grabbed at his hand, stopping him. It was the hardest thing she'd ever done. "No . . . Jesse. Please. I can't. I'm not ready for this." That was certainly the understatement of the decade! She doubted she'd ever be ready for the undisciplined way he made her feel. "I . . . This is too fast. It's too soon after—after . . ." She couldn't bring herself to mention the fact that she'd been so recently engaged, not when she was pressed so intimately against a man who wasn't her fiancé. "Jesse, *please.*"

He swore and rolled away from her, covering his face with a crooked arm. She was right, damn it! It was too fast. He was rushing her, acting like a clumsy idiot . . . A woman should be wooed, flirted with, charmed and flattered, lingered over until she was ready to take that final step and surrender herself freely. A man of his experience was supposed to know a woman shouldn't be jumped on, not the first time, or pushed into something she wasn't ready for, or convinced to do something in the heat of the moment she'd regret later. Sometimes it wasn't fair—his body was screaming that it wasn't fair at all!—but a woman's body was a gift she gave only when and if she was good and ready. And Kate Hightower had just made it very clear she wasn't ready.

This is too fast, she'd said, and he knew exactly what she meant. *It's too soon after—after...*

He lowered his arm to stare at her. She was sitting up, all flushed and flustered and suspiciously guilty looking as she tried to straighten her clothes and hair. "Too soon after what, Kate?"

Kate froze—and then resumed patting and tugging with single-minded attention. "Too soon after what, what?" she said, hoping to confuse the issue.

Jesse sat up. "You said, 'It's too soon after.' Too soon after what?" he repeated.

"Did I?" she said, still avoiding his eyes. "I guess I must have meant it was too soon after meeting you. What else could I have meant?"

Jesse reached out, grasping both her restless hands in one of his and cupping her cheek with the other. "I don't know, Kate," he said, staring into her wide, guilt-stricken brown eyes. "Why don't you tell me?"

"I didn't mean anything by it."

"Kate."

She took a deep breath. "Too soon after my engagement, okay? I meant it was too soon after my engagement."

Jesse felt something inside tighten hurtfully. "You said you weren't in love with him anymore."

"I'm not." Kate was emphatic on that point. "I don't think I ever was."

Jesse dropped his hands to his lap, thoroughly confused. "But then—" If she didn't love another man, wasn't mourning a broken engagement, why— "I don't understand."

"I broke my engagement three days ago," she said, suddenly determined to get it all out. The truth might make her sound hopelessly fickle and indecisive and just plain crazy, but it was the truth. "Last Thursday, to be exact. We were at the wedding rehearsal and I just panicked and ran. We were supposed to be married this afternoon." She looked at the slim gold watch on her left wrist. "The ceremony was supposed to start in about twenty minutes, actually. When it was over I would have been Mrs. Reed Wayne Sullivan the Third."

Jesse asked the only question he could think of at the moment. "Are you sorry you're not?"

"No." The answer came without a moment's hesitation. "No, I'm not." She looked into Jesse's eyes and smiled a kind of sweet, sad smile. "But it's still too soon after my engagement to be thinking of...of, ah, going to bed with another man. It would make me feel—" her shoulders shifted uneasily under the black-and-gold football jersey "—cheap, I guess. Like some kind of bed-hopping floozy."

"You could never be cheap," Jesse said, "and the way you feel right now proves it."

Well, he thought, *at least I know what she meant by "too soon after."* It was too soon after her broken engagement for a woman like Kate to let another man make love to her. Especially a man she'd only met two days ago.

Jesse sighed, resigning himself to several more days—or weeks!—of gentle wooing before she granted him the gift of total intimacy. "You're absolutely right," he said, reaching out to put his hands on her shoulders. "This is neither the time nor the place."

Kate stared at the blanket, wondering if she should tell him there would probably never be a right time and place for them. Wondering, too, why the thought brought her so much pain.

"And even if it was," he went on, his hands still on her shoulders, "things were moving entirely too fast. I— Kate, look at me."

"I can't."

"Sure you can, darlin'." He lifted her chin with his forefinger. "See?" His smile was slow and sweet and infinitely gentle. "Now was that so hard?"

She shrugged uneasily, uncomfortable with such close, intense scrutiny. Reed had never been one for gazing into her eyes to any great degree. Nor was anyone else in her family, except when they were trying to intimidate someone over a business deal.

"You haven't got anything to be embarrassed about, darlin'."

Shows how much you know, she thought, as pictures of what might have been happening between them if she hadn't come to her senses tumbled through her mind.

"Tell you what," Jesse said. "I'll make you a promise. The solemn promise of a Southern gentleman." He put his hand over his heart and smiled, trying to lighten the mood. "We'll take it nice and slow from now on. Real nice and easy until you say otherwise, okay?"

She shrugged again. How was she supposed to respond to something like that?

"Nothing's going to happen between us until you're ready for it to happen," Jesse said.

Oh, that's a real comfort, she thought. She wanted everything to happen between them. Everything that had never happened between her and Reed. Everything that could happen to a woman who wanted a man as much as she wanted Jesse.

"And the next time," Jesse said, "if there is a next time, I'll wait for your invitation." He drew a cross over his heart. "Word of honor."

Kate wondered miserably if Jesse had just saved from her own baser self, and then decided that, yes, he had. If he didn't make the move, then no move would be made because she wasn't brave enough to make it.

She wanted to hit him for being so damned noble.

7

MUCH TO KATE'S DISMAY, Jesse held fast to his promise not to push her into anything she wasn't ready for. Not that he stayed away from her and let her get on with figuring out her life, such as it was. Not at all. He was into more refined torture than that....

He came back to Secrets later that Sunday night, bringing beignets and coffee spiked with brandy. Under the guise of simple neighborliness he painted the trim on door frames and baseboards while craftily encouraging Kate and Lilac to reminisce about their college days while they finished painting the walls.

"I'll never forget the first time you introduced me to your family," Lilac said. "You took me home for Thanksgiving, remember? Every last livin' Hightower was there, including your great-aunt Katherine."

"It was her house," Kate interjected. "Thanksgiving is always held at Aunt Katherine's."

Lilac waved her to silence. "They took one look at me," she said to Jesse, "and decided I was leadin' their dutiful little ewe lamb down the path to—to . . ."

"Wholesale rebellion?" Jesse suggested dryly, without looking up from the section of baseboard he was painting.

"At the very least," Lilac agreed. "And I still don't understand why," she said, feigning a hurt look. "I was on my very best behavior."

"Which means you didn't try to flirt with Aunt Katherine's butler," Kate accused.

"I did, too." Lilac flicked paint at her. "And, I'll have you know, he winked at *me*."

"That's just a tick," Kate said, earning herself another flick of Lilac's paintbrush. She ignored it. "Edward was already well over sixty, even then," she said to Jesse, "but you know Lilac." She rolled her eyes. "She has to practice her wiles on every male within sight."

"I don't practice," Lilac said grandly. "I hone."

THE NEXT AFTERNOON, Jesse took Kate to lunch at the Court of Two Sisters and played with her fingers across the table while they ate pampano in a delicate lemon-lime sauce and talked about their families.

"Aunt Katherine is really my father's aunt, not mine," Kate said. "But she's more like his mother. She raised him after both his parents were killed in a car crash when he was six."

"She never married?"

Kate shook her head. "There's a supposedly secret family story that her heart was irreparably broken when her sweetheart was shot down over Germany in World War One, but no one really knows if it's true. Personally, I think she never married because she didn't want to lose control of the family fortune to a husband."

"Seems a little unusual that a woman in that day and age would be left in charge of a fortune in the first place."

"There was no one else," Kate said. "Her oldest brother was killed in the war, too. And the one remaining brother, after my grandparents died, didn't want anything to do with the family business." She smiled, lowering her voice as if imparting a deep, dark family secret that she didn't want anyone else to hear. "Great-Uncle Charles was an artist."

"Happens in the best of families," Jesse drawled.

Kate chuckled. "Yes, well . . . anyway, according to family legend, Aunt Katherine took up the reins of both the family and what was left of the business after the Depression, and somehow managed to salvage a good deal of the family fortune for the next generation," Kate said, pride evident in her voice. "It's thanks to her that we—all the current Hightower cousins," she explained, "have any kind of trust fund available. I used part of mine for college and—" she grinned conspiratorially "—invested the rest in Secrets. Much to Aunt Katherine's disgust," she added.

"You love her very much," Jesse said.

"Yes, I do." Kate sighed. "Even when I'm shaking in my shoes, waiting for the ax to fall."

"Are you shaking in your shoes now?"

Kate cocked a questioning eyebrow at him.

"Isn't she going to drop the ax on you for deserting your fiancé at the altar?"

Kate winced just thinking about it. "Undoubtedly," she said and changed the subject to *his* family.

THE NEXT EVENING he took her out for dinner and dancing on a Mississippi riverboat.

"Five years," he said as they stood side by side on the deck after dinner, staring out over the dark, moon-kissed water. "That's a long time to be engaged."

"Yes," Kate agreed, "I guess it is. It didn't seem like it at the time, though. I mean—" she reached out and brushed a strand of windblown hair out of her eyes "—there was always something else coming up...you know, at the office or whatever. Some big fund-raiser I was all tied up with. Or Reed would have this big case he was working on—Reed's a lawyer," she explained, "or some cousin or other was graduating from college or getting married and the calendar was too crowded to schedule another big family event."

"You could have eloped."

Kate sighed—rather wistfully, Jesse thought—and shook her head. "We didn't really want to get married. Or, at least, I didn't." She turned, leaning with both elbows on the rail behind her, her head thrown back to let the breeze play freely with her hair. "I can see that quite clearly now," she said, hoping Jesse would take the opportunity she offered him to kiss her.

He didn't.

AT HIS REQUEST, Kate met him at his salon the next day for "a quick lunch" since they both had busy schedules. She arrived a bit early, catching him in the process of blow drying the waist-length mane of a very blond, very beautiful client. At least, Kate amended sourly, the woman's hair was beautiful. The way she was bent over in the stylist's chair, with the top of her head nearly touching Jesse's jeans-clad groin, it was impossible to see her face.

"Jesse'll be about ten minutes, Miz Hightower," Annabelle said from behind the reception desk. "Can I get you something while you wait? An iced tea?"

"No, thank you," Kate said absently, her eyes on the woman tossing back about a foot and a half of blond hair as she straightened in Jesse's chair.

Does he have to stand so close? Kate wondered, not even bothering to deny the feeling of jealousy that coursed through her at the sight. *Does he have to run his fingers through her hair like that?* she demanded silently, tacitly admitting that she wanted his hands in *her* hair. *Does he have to smile at her like she's the only woman on earth?* she fumed, inexplicably wanting to be the sole recipient of his attentive, wickedly charming smiles.

He looked up just then, as if feeling her eyes on him. His smile widened by several degrees, warming her to her toes.

"Five minutes," he mouthed, holding his hand up, fingers spread, to show her how much longer he'd be.

He was done in three.

Finishing his client's hair with a quick spritz of aerosol spray, he held a mirror for her to view the results from all angles and then assisted her from the stylist's chair with a quick kiss to the back of her hand and a laughing remark—all without revealing his burning impatience to have her on her way so he could greet his lunch date.

"Sorry to keep you waiting, darlin'," he said, taking Kate's hand to tuck it into the crook of his elbow. It felt like days, rather than mere hours, since he'd seen her last. "Hungry?" he asked, smiling at her.

For you, Kate thought, her fingers curling against the bare, warm, hair-dusted skin of his forearm. "Starving," she said, trying not to drool.

He took her at her word, buying her a plate of red beans and rice—a traditional New Orleans meal, he said—before whisking her off for a quick tour of the New Orleans Jazz Museum.

Fuming with the rapidly escalating desire to grab him by his ears and demand that he kiss her, Kate strolled along beside him like the lady she'd been

raised to be, endeavoring to be amused by his color-
ful commentary on the Mardi Gras exhibit.

THE NEXT DAY he took her to the Voodoo Museum and
Gift Shop, where she purchased what turned out to
be a love charm.

"You put it under your pillow," the saleswoman said
with a wink, as if she knew exactly what was bothering Kate. "It'll bring your lover to you in the night."

Kate thanked the woman for her unsolicited advice, all the while telling herself she had no need or
desire for love charms. But, that night, feeling foolish
in the extreme, she put it under her pillow.

It didn't work.

She threw it away the next morning, before Lilac
could see it and tease her, telling herself it was all for
the best, anyway, that she didn't really want Jesse in
her bed and that, all things considered, she probably
shouldn't go out with him anymore. To continue to
do so, when there was no future in it, when she would
be going back to her life in Boston in another week,
was foolish in the extreme. But the next night when
Jesse arrived on Lilac's front porch to pick her up, she
was ready and waiting.

He was dressed more formally than she'd ever seen
him in a pair of black pleated-front slacks, a loose
black silk crepe-de-chine shirt with a skinny steel-gray
tie and a slightly oversize, immaculately white dinner jacket, in the 1920s style. The diamond stud an-

choring his tie matched the one in his left ear. On anyone else the outfit would have looked theatrical and overdone. On Jesse, with his shaggy blond hair just touching his collar in back and his warm golden skin, it was elegance personified.

Kate felt positively dowdy in her ivory silk shirtwaist and Lilac's pearls. Excusing herself on the pretext of getting her purse, she hurried into the bedroom. But what could she do, really, she thought, fluffing her hair with both hands as she stared into the cheval mirror. A shirtwaist, silk or not, was still a shirtwaist, and not terribly exciting.

And she wanted, very much, for Jesse to find her as exciting as she found him.

"Try showin' a little skin," Lilac said from behind her.

Kate met the blonde's eyes in the mirror. "Skin?"

"Kate, honey, you've got one of the great bosoms of the Western world. Show it off a little." She grinned impishly. "I guarantee Jesse'll notice."

Kate raised her hand to the buttons on the front of her dress and released the first one, then, more hesitantly, the second.

"One more," Lilac said. "Flash a little of that cleavage."

Feeling greatly daring, Kate did as Lilac advised. The pearl necklace slid inside her collar as she released the third button, and came to rest against the warm creaminess of her chest and the beginning swell of her lush breasts.

"Perfect," Lilac said gleefully. "You'll have him drooling in his soup."

"You think so?" Kate said hesitantly. She'd never had a man drool over her, period, let alone into his soup.

"Guaranteed," Lilac assured her.

Smiling at her image, feeling suddenly sleek and feline and female, Kate picked up her purse and left the room.

He took her to dinner at Antoine's, a restaurant so famous she'd heard of it even in Boston. They sat at a beautifully laid table, in a dining room filled with romance and Mardi Gras memorabilia, and ordered from a menu written in French from a waiter who took their order without ever once writing anything down.

"Eddie's been a waiter at Antoine's for most of his adult life," Jesse said, trying not to stare too obviously at the inviting shadow between her breasts.

Her pearls were playing peek-a-boo with the open collar of her silk dress, gleaming and sliding against her even silkier skin with every slight movement she made. It was going to be damned hard—in more ways than one—to keep his promise not to push when she looked the way she did tonight.

"According to one of our family legends, he served dinner to my parents the night my father proposed to my mother," Jesse told her, trying to distract himself by making conversation, "right here at this very table."

Kate leaned forward. "You're kidding," she said, enchanted.

"No, I'm not." The pearls were dangling between her breasts, making him wonder how he could ever have thought her prim. She was lush and seductive and tantalizingly provocative. "Eddie's been here since—"

"That's not what I meant. I meant—" she caught the warm, sensual look in his eyes across the candlelit table and had no doubt, just then, that he found her wildly exciting. Wondering just how far she could push before he'd do some pushing of his own, she reached up and touched the pearls that rested again her skin, lightly running her fingertip over their creamy roundness. His eyes followed the movement. "You know what I meant," she said softly.

"Well, I wasn't kidding about that, either." He reached across the small table as he spoke and took her hand in his. "I never kid about something as serious as tradition and romance," he said, lifting her fingers to his lips for a lingering kiss.

"Hope I'm not interruptin' another proposal here, Mr. de Vallerin, sir," the waiter said as he deftly slid their plates onto the table. "But these here oysters Rockefeller are going to get mighty cold if I wait much longer."

"No, no proposal, Eddie." Jesse released her hand without releasing her eyes. "Not tonight, anyway."

Every nerve in Kate's body went on red alert. *Not tonight? What did he mean, not tonight? Was he implying there would be a proposal forthcoming on some other night? Or even that he might be proposing to her on this hypothetical other night?*

"Try the oysters Rockefeller, darlin'," Jesse said, bringing her back to earth. "They were invented at Antoine's, you know."

Kate ate her oysters, and her grilled lamb chops with pommes soufflées and string beans and her sinfully rich chocolate mousse and told herself not to dwell on it.

He was just flirting with his talk of proposals, was all. And even if he was, by some huge stretch of the imagination, more serious than that, well, she'd just gotten rid of one fiancé and wasn't in the market for another one. No, what she was in the market for was—

What?

That passionate, but very finite, fling Lilac had suggested?

Well, no, not exactly. She didn't go in for passionate flings with sexy strangers, no matter how intense the physical attraction.

A lover, then?

A lover was something more than a fling, at least in her definition of things. The word lover implied a certain level of emotional attachment, a degree of ... of fondness.

She glanced across the table at her dinner companion.

Was she fond of Jesse de Vallerin?

Oh, yes, came the instantaneous thought. If the feeling that heated her blood and clouded her judgment every time she looked at him could be labeled mere fondness, then, yes, she was most definitely fond of Jesse de Vallerin.

A lover, then, she thought.

But did she dare?

He smiled at her across the table just then, his lips curving upward in that heartbreakingly sweet, charmingly wicked way of his, his eyes crinkling at the corners with the sleepy sensuality that was never far from the surface. "To you, darlin'," he said, lifting his brandy glass to touch the rim to hers.

Oh, yes, she thought, silently returning the salute. *I dare.*

And later tonight, she decided, when he took her back to his apartment for the coffee he hadn't thought to offer her the last time, she wouldn't balk like some frightened virgin and insist on being taken home. No, she'd find some subtle, feminine, sexy way to let him know she was his for the taking. To release him, as it were, from his promise not to push her into anything she didn't want or wasn't ready for.

She was ready now. More than ready.

But when later finally came, he didn't give her a chance to show him she'd changed her mind. He took her on a carriage ride through the Quarter with a loquacious driver who was more than happy to fill her in on any history or legends Jesse may have missed, and then to the brightly lit Café du Monde for chicory coffee and beignets. Not once did he suggest or give her the chance to suggest, that she come back to his place with him. The evening ended at Lilac's front door with a quick kiss that wouldn't have been out of place between siblings except for the way it made her feel.

Stunned, Kate stood on the porch and watched him drive away with her mouth all but hanging open, unable to decide if the feelings coursing through her owed more to disappointment, frustration or pure feminine pique at having the unprecedented offer of her precious self with no strings attached refused before she'd even made it.

Lilac glanced up from the book she was reading as Kate opened the front door, took one look and knew immediately that her best friend from college was as mad as a spitting cat. "Trouble in paradise?" she asked.

Kate opened her mouth to deny it but, "Yes!" she said and threw her purse onto the couch so hard it bounced onto the floor.

Lilac raised an eyebrow at that and, without a word, put her book aside. "Come tell me all about it," she said, patting the sofa next to her.

Kate preferred to pace. "That man has no sensitivity," she fumed. A man with any sensitivity at all would have sensed that she wanted...that she was... "Not one ounce of sensitivity in his whole gorgeous body!"

"Uh-huh," Lilac said, leaning over to pick up the purse. She put it on the glass-topped white wicker coffee table. "What did he do?"

"Nothing! That's what he did. Absolutely nothing."

"You're mad at him for doin' nothin'?"

"Yes! No! I mean— Hell, I don't know what I mean." She stopped pacing and glared at her hostess. "You can just wipe that smug grin off your face, Lilac Prescott. This is all your fault."

Lilac wiped the grin off her face, but seemed unable to erase it from her eyes. "What's all my fault?" she said sweetly.

"Everything!"

"That's kind of all-encompassin', honey. Could you narrow it down a bit?"

"You got me drunk—"

Lilac gave her a look.

"Well, you encouraged me to get drunk, and then you dragged me down here to New Orleans and made me buy new clothes and get my hair cut and . . . and go out with Jesse."

"I most certainly did not," Lilac said to the last charge. "You did that all on your own."

"You introduced me to him," she accused, making it sound as if it were tantamount to leading her into a life of sin.

"Yes," Lilac agreed. "I introduced you. So how does that make everything my fault?"

"Because it—because he—" She flopped down onto the couch and put her head in her hands. "Oh, Lilac, what am I going to do about him?"

"Well, that depends," Lilac said, selflessly forbearing to mention that she'd already answered that question for her confused houseguest.

"On what?" Kate demanded.

"What do you want to do about him?"

Kate gave a very unladylike snort. "Guess."

LILAC'S ADVICE WAS, as usual, practical and straight to the point. "Well, honey, I guess it's up to you to take the initiative if you want him so all-fired bad," she said when Kate finally got around to confiding the exact nature of her problem with Jesse. "Heaven knows, that's one thing you've never lacked."

And Lilac was absolutely right, Kate thought, as she lay in bed that night in a welter of rumpled sheets and frustrated desire. Initiative could have been her middle name if she hadn't already had too many others. Initiative and determination and clear-thinking intelligence; she had them all, she just hadn't been using them lately. She'd let herself be side-tracked by her own hidebound Boston-bred conventions and—well, might as well face it—by Jesse's enormous sex appeal and her own overwhelming reaction to it.

Well, she'd put Boston behind her, at least for the present, and it was time her hormones were put to better use than confusing her. It was time she stopped acting like some wimpy Southern belle, she thought, with mental apologies to Lilac—time she grabbed the bull by the horns, so to speak, and went after what she wanted.

She was a Hightower, wasn't she?

And she wanted a change, didn't she? A chance to look at life from a different perspective before she decided what she was going to do with the rest of hers. And Jesse, bless his gorgeous hide and misplaced chivalry, certainly had a different perspective on things.

Kate punched her pillow into a more comfortable shape and, with her goal firmly in mind, began planning her seduction strategy with all the care and attention to detail she'd been trained to give to wooing contributors to the various Hightower charities.

Jesse was a man who took pleasure in the sensual things in life. Well, then, she would drown him in sensation!

She started the next afternoon with a new bath oil, something sexy and sultry and as unlike her crisp Boston scent or Lilac's signature fragrance as she could find. And then, when she was sweet-smelling and silky soft all over, she slipped into a pair of lacy white panties, a beribboned garter belt, and real silk stockings from Secrets stock that made her feel as sweetly, deliciously wicked as Jesse looked. Braless, she stepped into the eyelet sundress that Lilac had said was so perfect for her. Looking at her reflection in the mirror, she had to admit that Lilac had been right, as usual.

The dress was perfect for her.

She twirled in front of the cheval mirror, making the ruffled edge of the skirt unfurl around her stockinged thighs, delighted with herself and the frothy mint-green dress and the frightening, funny, utterly feminine way she felt inside. The doorbell rang as she was standing there, admiring the fit of the dress and the way the color complemented her warm, creamy complexion and brought out the red highlights in her hair. She started at the sound, lifting her gaze to meet her eyes in the mirror.

This was it.

This was the point where she could still change her mind. But she knew, with a bone deep certainty, that she'd regret it for the rest of her life if she did. She wanted Jesse de Vallerin in a way she'd never wanted anyone or anything else, ever. It made no sense and maybe it was even a little crazy but if she didn't do something about it now, while she had the chance, she'd spend the rest of her life wondering.

She took a deep, calming breath and then let it out slowly, leaning over to pick up her purse from where it lay on the bed. Opening it, she checked to make sure she had the package of condoms she'd forced herself to purchase that afternoon when she bought the bath oil. They were there, a variety pack, tucked between the plastic case that held her travel toothbrush and the purse-sized package of tissues she always carried. She was ready for anything.

"I hope," she murmured, giving herself a final, confidence-boosting glance in the mirror before sailing out the bedroom door to greet the man she was determined to seduce before the night was over.

He'd arrived by streetcar again, at Kate's specific request. "Lilac mentioned how impossible it is to get a parking space in the Quarter on weekends," she'd said, and suggested they could walk over to his apartment for his car when it was time to drive her back to the Garden District, just like he had the last time. It was, she thought, as plausible and innocent a reason as any for going to his place; he didn't need to know—yet—that she had no intention of letting him drive her to Lilac's until her virtue had been thoroughly compromised.

They ate on the Embers balcony, sipping Pernod while they waited for their steaks to broil and watching the good-natured craziness slowly build at the intersection of St. Peter and Bourbon streets as the twilight grew darker.

There was something different about her tonight, Jesse thought, watching her over the candlelight that flickered in the lamp between them. He'd noticed it the minute she walked out of Lilac's bedroom. It wasn't just the dress, frillier and more deliciously, deliberately feminine than any he'd ever seen her wear before, or the heady new scent that was almost dizzying in its sensual appeal. It was *her*.

She moved differently; leaning forward, her elbows on the table as she ran a fingertip around the edge of her glass, her long, silky legs seductively crossing and uncrossing, her smooth, bare shoulders lifting as she spoke, her head tilting. She laughed differently; soft, husky murmurs of sound that hinted at intimacy and shared secrets. She looked at him differently; quick, darting glances from under the veil of her lashes, shy sideways gazes that lingered on his hands or his lips when she thought he wasn't looking. And she touched him; an innocent press of her knee against his as they rode the streetcar, an accidental nudge of her hip as they walked side by side through the Quarter, the tantalizing, feather-light brush of her fingers on the back of his hand when he reached across the table to pour cream in her coffee.

It delighted him and drove him crazy at the same time because he wasn't sure what was causing it. In another woman he'd have sworn it was a deliberate come-on. But Kate did it so . . . so innocently that he couldn't be sure. Her new attitude toward him could just as easily mean she was getting more comfortable around him, and wasn't so much on her guard. And that was good, too. It was, after all, what he'd been working toward for the past few days.

He was still pondering the change in her when the check came, wondering if he might press his suit, just a little now that she— His signature squiggled untidily over the edge of the credit card receipt as the significance of that last thought hit him.

Suit, he thought. *As in suing for her hand? As in—* he swallowed—*courtship?*

He looked across the table at her, a question in his eyes. She smiled, looking at him from under her lashes as she idly traced the edge of her coffee cup with her fingertip. Jesse felt his heart turn clean over.

Well, I'll be damned, he thought, *I'm courting a Yankee!*

He didn't even recall falling in love. He'd always thought he'd know the exact moment when it happened, that he'd be able to say later, when he was recounting the story to his children, "And that's when I fell in love with your mother." But, somehow, the fact that he couldn't quite put his finger on the moment he'd tumbled into love seemed exactly, perfectly right. He smiled beatifically.

"Jesse?" Kate said hesitantly. He was staring at her with the stunned expression of a man who'd been hit between the eyes with a piece of lead pipe. "Is anything wrong?"

He shook his head to clear it. "Not a thing in the world," he assured her, bending his head to finish signing the charge slip.

He'd have to continue to take it slow, he told himself. Just because he'd been hit by a thunderbolt didn't mean she was ready to hear or make declarations of undying love. She wasn't the kind of woman who could be swept off her feet; her ingrained cautiousness wouldn't let her trust an emotion that happened too fast. She was the kind of woman who needed time, patience and tender wooing before she'd let herself do anything so rash as fall in love. Well, nice and easy was what he'd promised her. Nice and easy was what she'd get.

Even if it killed him.

"Ready to go?" he said, setting the pen and charge slip aside.

Kate nodded. She was so ready she was about to explode. She'd been ready for days.

Jesse got to his feet, solicitously holding her chair for her as she rose.

"Can we walk a bit?" Kate said as they made their way down the restaurant steps and onto the teeming sidewalk.

"Darlin'," he said, taking her hand to tuck it into the crook of his arm as they started down the street, "we can do anything your little heart desires."

Kate hoped he meant that literally.

8

BY UNSPOKEN MUTUAL CONSENT, they strolled away from the frenzied action on Bourbon Street, down St. Peter, where the line to get into Pat O'Brian's was already three deep and twenty long, and wandered in the general direction of the levee. They were both unnaturally quiet.

Jesse was contemplating all the delicious nuances of courtship. Eagerly anticipating Kate's final surrender, he wondered if a week was enough time to lead her into loving him or if he was going to have to follow her to Boston to plead his case. And what was her family going to say when he claimed her as his?

Kate, meanwhile, was wondering just what in the hell was wrong with her seduction technique. She'd been flirting and sending out signals like crazy and Jesse, except for that one long moment when he'd stared at her as if she had two heads, was acting just the same as he always did. Charming, sexy, considerate and sweet. In short, a perfect gentleman.

It wasn't that she'd expected him to jump on her or anything like that—Jesse wasn't the type to lunge at a woman—but she had expected some sort of acknowledgment of her efforts. She looked at him from under her lashes. Hadn't he noticed? Or wasn't he interested, that way, any longer?

He looked at her and smiled. It was that same slightly idiotic, beatific smile he'd given her across the dinner table. It warmed her to the bone and made her wonder what new tortures he was thinking up to tantalize her with.

"Warm enough?" he murmured, tenderly touching the slender hand that lay in the crook of his arm.

On fire. Kate nodded.

"Good," he said and squeezed her hand, drawing it more securely between his arm and body.

He was still interested, all right, she thought, relieved. He just wasn't doing anything about that interest.

And it was all her fault.

Like a fool, she'd exacted that stupid promise from him last Sunday after he'd kissed her into a state of near panic. And, like some chivalrous knight of old, he'd given her his word as a Southern gentleman to take it "nice and easy... real nice and slow until you say otherwise." Something told her that, like any self-respecting knight, he took his word very seriously.

Did that mean she was actually going to have to say, out loud, what she wanted?

"I don't think I can," she mumbled. None of her carefully laid plans involved actually *saying* she wanted to go to bed with him.

"Beg pardon?" Jesse said. His hand came up to cover hers again. "What did you say?"

"It's a lovely night," she said.

"Lovely," he agreed.

Seduction, she thought dismally, *is a lot harder than it looks.*

Maybe she should just reach down and put her hand on his, ah . . . thigh. Or open her purse, pull out one of those condoms she'd purchased that afternoon and hand it to him. That'd get her intentions across in no uncertain terms!

"Any place in particular you'd like to go?" Jesse said in her ear.

Your place, she thought. "Such as?" she asked.

"Another jazz club? A show?" *My place.* "A bar?" he suggested. "We could stop in someplace for an after-dinner drink."

"No. Thank you. What we had with dinner is more than enough." Inspiration struck. "Actually," she said, "what I'd really like is another cup of coffee."

"I think that can be arranged. The Café du Monde is just a couple of blocks away."

"I don't feel like the Café du Monde," she said. "Too bright and noisy."

"Shall we try the lounge at the Royal Orleans?"

Kate shook her head. "Too many people."

"Where then?"

Kate took a deep breath. Drastic times called for drastic measures. "How about your place?"

Jesse felt his pulses quicken. "My place?" he said carefully, wondering suddenly, hopefully if his self-imposed waiting period was about to come to an end or if she was really only suggesting a cup of coffee.

"You do have the makings for coffee, don't you?"

"Yes."

"And that gorgeous little courtyard to drink it in?"

"Yes."

She smiled at him. "Good, because I've never had coffee in a New Orleans courtyard."

Just coffee then, he thought. *Damn.*

But when they got to his courtyard and he invited her to have a seat while he went upstairs to make the coffee she'd requested, she stopped him.

"Jesse," she said.

He turned on the bottom step to look at her. She was right behind him, one hand curved around the base of the lantern at the bottom of the stairs, the other holding her purse at her side. She looked shy and uncertain and unbearably sweet.

"What?" he said, smiling tenderly.

Now or never, she thought; she wouldn't have the courage to put herself through this again. "I don't really want any coffee." *There, that should be plain enough.*

It wasn't.

"What do you want?" His voice was a soft murmur of sound. He waited tensely for her answer, not trusting himself to anticipate her. He wanted her too much to trust his own perceptions where she was concerned.

"I want—" She swallowed. *Why is he being so obtuse?* "I want—" She'd never asked anyone to kiss her before but there was really only one way to say it. She said it quickly, the words tumbling over each other in her effort to get them out. "I want you to kiss me."

He stood there on the step for just a heartbeat's worth of time, staring at her as if one of them had lost their mind.

"Jesse?" she said hesitantly.

He swooped down the single step, taking her into his arms before the sound of his name had died in the air between them. "And after I kiss you?" he whispered. He didn't want to carry her off to bed if all she was asking for was a kiss or two in the moonlight. "And after I kiss you?" he insisted when she remained silent.

"And after you kiss me, I want you to forget that stupid promise and make lo—" No, not make love; that wasn't what they were going to do. She needed, for her own sake, not to confuse the issue in her mind. They were going to scratch a mutual itch. "Take me to bed," she finished, wondering why she didn't quite believe her own assessment of the situation.

Jesse's laugh was low and intimate, rife with masculine triumph. "I never promised not to make love to you," he said against her lips, unconsciously choosing the term he preferred for what they were about to do. "I only promised to take it slow and easy." He cupped her head between his hand, holding her still while he ran his tongue across her bottom lip. "Do you like it slow and easy, darlin'?"

Kate sighed and wrapped her arms around his lean waist, unaware that she still held her purse clutched in one hand. "Just kiss me, dammit," she demanded, coming up on tiptoe to bring her mouth against his.

He kissed her, deeply, thoroughly, completely, plunging his tongue into her mouth in imitation of the act they'd both been thinking about since they first laid eyes on each other. It lasted for a short eternity, heads turning and tilting; lips clinging and parting and coming back to cling again; teeth nibbling and nipping; tongues searching out the sweetness, savoring the tastes and textures of each other; voices murmuring incoherently, sighing. And then, finally, Jesse drew away and took her hand in his.

"Let's go upstairs," he said shakily, "and do this right."

Kate followed him wordlessly, amazed that she could still put one foot in front of the other with her heart thudding against the wall of her chest and her body pulsing in time to its labored beat. He led her up the wooden stairs, across the gallery, through his dark, shadowed apartment to his bedroom.

It was high-ceilinged, cool and sparsely, elegantly furnished. The huge bed was made up with crisp white sheets and nothing else, flanked by a pair of red-lacquered Chinese chests used as nightstands, facing a large polished pine armoire. A fan-back wicker chair and a display of Mardi Gras masks took up one wall. A double set of French doors opening onto the fanciful wrought-iron balcony that ran the length of the building took up another. Silver moonlight and the golden glow of the streetlights filtered into the room through the floor-length gossamer curtains, providing more than enough illumination for them to see each other by.

"Are you sure?" Jesse said, looking into her face as they stood by the edge of the bed.

Kate nodded.

"Say it," he ordered.

"I'm sure."

He lifted her hand to his lips, kissed the palm and pressed it against his cheek. "I'm glad."

Kate's smile was tremulous. "So am I."

He brought her closer by the hand he held, drawing it up and behind his head. Her palm brushed over the sparkling diamond in his left ear and the shaggy hair at his nape to curve against the warm, firm column of his neck. He held her hand cupped in his and rubbed against her touch like a great, golden cat, demanding to be petted.

Kate murmured and moved to snuggle closer, more than eager to oblige him. The corner of her purse nearly poked him in the eye as she brought her other hand up to encircle his neck.

He backed off. "Let's put this down, shall we?" he said, reaching to take it from her so he could put it on the bedside table.

Kate shook her head. From everything she'd read lately, now, before things became too heated and passionate, was the time to get this particular step out of the way. She fumbled for the clasp. "I have—that is—" She shoved her hand inside the purse and pulled out a small box. "Here," she said, thrusting it at him.

Automatically, Jesse took it. "What—" he began, looking at the package he held. A second later, he lifted his startled gaze to hers. "Condoms?" he said, turning it over in his long fingers. A corner of his mouth quirked up. "The variety pack?"

"Well, I didn't know what size or—" she trailed off, more embarrassed than she'd ever been in her life but determined to go through with it "—or anything and I—I don't want you to think—" She didn't want him to think she carried them around with her just in case she got lucky. "That is—" *How on earth did people do this all the time?* "I bought them this afternoon," she said in a small voice.

He just stood there, looking at the box of condoms in his hand with a half amused, half incredulous expression on his face. He was feeling amazingly, incredibly pleased. He'd been worrying about pushing her into something she wasn't ready for and she'd gone out and bought condoms for him. Not many women would do that. But then, not many woman were Kate Hightower—his prim, sensible, utterly adorable Kate.

"It's not that I think there's anything wrong with you," she hastened to assure him, taking his silence for displeasure. Lord knew, Reed would have been highly displeased over the implications inherent in that one little box. "They're as much for your protection as mine." The words ran together as she tried to explain. "I mean—"

He put his fingers over her lips, stopping her. "I know what you mean."

She sagged with very visible relief.

"And I appreciate the gesture. It was very practical of you." It was also totally unnecessary; like any prudent single man, he had a supply of the things in his nightstand, but she didn't need to know that. Without turning around, he reached behind him and placed the box, and her purse, on the bedside table. Then he shrugged out of his jacket and tossed it across the wicker chair. It slid to the polished hardwood floor. "Now," he said, capturing her hands in his, "shall we begin again?"

"Yes, please," Kate mumbled, still embarrassed. Not embarrassed enough to call a halt to the whole thing but enough to make her feel uncomfortable. It had all been going so well before she'd produced that damned box! And it was probably totally unnecessary. She was on the Pill, after all, and Jesse wasn't exactly in a high risk group. Still, a body couldn't be too careful these days; it was only good sense to take precautions.

"Hey, darlin'." Jesse wiggled her hands from side to side. "Relax."

"I'm relaxed."

"No, you're not." He drew both her hands up behind his head, folding them over each other so they overlapped at the back of his neck, then ran his palms, slowly, caressingly, down the silky length of her bare arms to her shoulders. "But give me, say—" his palms skimmed to her elbows and back again "—an hour, and I promise you will be."

Kate felt her skin begin to heat with something that burned away any lingering embarrassment. Practicality and good sense were instantly forgotten, along with everything else except Jesse and the way he made her feel.

"An hour?" she murmured, closing her eyes and tilting her head as his mouth descended toward hers. "That long?"

He kissed her very lightly, brushing his lips back and forth over hers. "Forty minutes?" he suggested, keeping a tantalizing five inches between their bodies while his hands worked between them, busily unbuttoning his shirt. His knuckles brushed against her breasts.

Bemused, Kate shook her head, just to see what he would say.

"Thirty?" Another butterfly brush of his lips accompanied the word. She felt his fingers on the back of her neck. "Anything less and you're really rushing me," he warned. "I don't do my best work when I'm rushed."

Kate murmured something about certainly not wanting to rush him and returned the nuzzling caress of his lips.

"I knew you were a reasonable woman. Ah, there—"

Something slithered over her shoulders.

"That's got it," he said with satisfaction as the top of her halter dress slid around her waist.

He followed its descent with his hands, trailing his sensitive fingertips over her shoulders and chest—"Heated silk," he marveled—down the full slopes of her breasts—"Exquisite," he murmured—to pluck delicately at the twin peaks of her tight pinkish-brown nipples.

Kate moaned softly as the heat curled through her, spreading out in lazy spirals from his teasing fingers to her brain and her belly and beyond. Her head fell back and she arched her spine, offering her breasts more fully to his touch. Her hands hung, arms lax, wrists as limp as wilted leaves, over his shoulders. She watched him from under lowered lashes, as moved by the rapt, intense expression on his face as by the way he touched her. His words, soft and honey-sweet, only intensified the emotions spiraling through her.

"I knew it would be like this," he said, watching her nipples harden as he rolled them between his fingers. He felt the heat, too, burning his fingertips as he touched her, forking through him like lightning. "Knew you'd be like this. I could tell by looking at your mouth. You have a courtesan's mouth," he told her. "Did you know that, darlin'? Skin like a sweet, rosy baby—" he cupped his palms around the fullness of her breasts for a moment then slid his hands upward to gently, reverently, cup her cheeks "—and a courtesan's mouth." He traced the outline of her lips with a fingertip. "Lush and sweet and tempting as sin," he murmured hotly. "It's a mouth made to bring a man to his knees, darlin', and make him beg for a taste."

He slid his hands downward, caressing her neck and shoulders, her full, thrusting breasts and the soft, silky skin of her narrow rib cage. Spreading his hands wide, his fingers on her back and his thumbs resting just above the waistband of her dress, he drew her toward him. Their bare torsos touched, her soft, full, sensitized breasts flattening against his hard, hair-whorled chest. They both made little sounds of pleasure at that exquisite skin-to-skin contact. He moved his hands around to her bare back, palms flat, fingers wide, and pressed her closer.

"Give me your mouth, Kate," he commanded, just before he took it. "Let me taste your sweetness."

Kate melted against him, lips parted, fingers sliding through his hair, and gave her all. Her mouth, her mind, her body and, all unknowing, her guarded, yearning heart. His tongue brushed over her lips first, as if preparing them for its entry, then slid inside her mouth, languid and seeking and devastatingly thorough. She felt claimed by his kiss. Possessed. Wanted with an intensity that was almost as frightening as it was exciting.

This was how it was supposed to be, she exalted silently, wanting him with an ache that thrilled her. *This* was how she was meant to feel.

She strained against him, tightening her hands in his hair in a vain attempt to bring him closer, but it was impossible. They were already as close as two people could be unless he was inside her.

Inside her.

The words echoed through her desire-fogged brain.

She wanted him inside her.

Now.

"Easy." He lifted his mouth just far enough to make himself understood. "Easy, darlin'," he crooned. "We'll get to it." His drawl was thicker, deeper, in his passion. He ran his hands down her back to the tight waist of her dress. "We'll get to everything."

The zipper rasped downward.

He slipped his hands inside the opening it made, burrowing under the gathered eyelet to curve around her bottom. He pressed her to him for a moment, hard against his aching erection, and then moved back a step, letting the dress slide to the floor. It billowed around her ankles in a mint-green cloud. He followed it down, crouching, knees splayed, to skim his palms over her thighs and—

The lace panties and garter belt were a surprise. A delightful surprise. He'd always liked feminine fripperies and fancies; lace and bows and soft, silky fabrics said "woman" to him, and lingerie of almost any kind was a visual turn-on simply because of the intimacy involved, but this . . . ! The innocence of white lace and pink bows combined with the calculated sexiness of the garter belt, especially on a woman as tightly reined in as Kate appeared to be, almost knocked him out.

Sweetness and sin, he thought, wondering if she wore underclothes like this all the time, or if they'd been donned just for him.

He looked up at her from his crouched position, his fingers on the backs of her thighs, his thumbs touching the pink bows on her garters, his eyes full of devilment, intending to tease her about the secrets she hid under her clothes.

She was blushing so rosily even her breasts were pink, telling him without words that she'd dressed herself this way for him.

Jesse grinned wickedly. "You ought to blush," he chided her lazily. "Tempting a mortal man with all this." He flicked a pink bow with his thumb. "Boggling his poor befuddled brain with visions of lewd and lascivious acts."

"You like it," she said, with the air of someone who hadn't been completely sure he would.

"Oh, darlin'—" he pressed a hard, quick kiss on the scrap of cobwebby lace that covered her woman's mound "—I *love* it." He rocked back on his heels. "And I'm going to love taking it off you even more." He skimmed his hands the rest of the way down her legs. "One piece at a time," he said, cupping her heel. "Starting with your shoes. Lift up."

Kate rested her hands on his shoulders, lifting one foot then the other, as he took her strappy white sandals off and set them aside. She kept her hands on his shoulders as he came to his feet, sliding them under the open collar of his shirt and down his arms, baring his torso as he rose in front of her. He was as beautiful as some ancient, legendary god. All golden and hard and hairy in exactly the right places.

"I'm going to enjoy undressing you, too," she said. "One—" she leaned forward and pressed a light, open-mouthed kiss on the hard, hair-dusted curve of his left pectoral "—piece—" she kissed his right pectoral "—at—" her lips trailed a bit lower down, covering his flat male nipple "—a—" his other nipple "—time," she finished, stretching up to press her open mouth to the pulse pounding double-time at the base of his throat. Her breasts brushed against the moist spots she'd left on his skin. It was like touching two live wires together in a thunderstorm.

Instant electricity.

Instant need.

With identical groans, they reached to bring their bodies closer. Hands stroking and kneading, lips fused, open-mouthed and greedy, loins pressed tight, they fell together on the bed. Jesse hit the mattress first, then rolled, bringing Kate beneath him. Her legs opened, taking his lean, jeans-clad hips between them. He ground his erection against her. She whimpered and clutched at his back, reaching down with both hands to press him closer.

Closer.

The same thought was in both their minds.

They had to get closer.

Jesse eased away from her, rolling to the side so he could reach his fly.

Kate rolled with him, clinging like a limpet. "No."

"Zipper," he rasped, his face buried in the fragrance of her neck. Strands of reddish brown hair were sticking to his cheek.

"No," she said again, knowing only that he was pulling away. She squirmed on top of him, intent on keeping their bodies plastered together.

Low, frustrated laughter rippled through him. "I've got to get my jeans off," he panted.

She went still for a moment. "Oh," she said, like a surprised child. "Okay." She pushed herself upright with a hand on his chest, her legs astride him, shaking her hair back as she wriggled downward to straddle his thighs. "I'll do it."

The metal waistband button popped open with a single tug. She reached for the zipper.

He groaned as the backs of her fingers rubbed against the hard, aching bulge of his arousal. "I've died and gone to heaven."

She looked at him through a lock of hair. "What?"

"You're killing me, darlin'."

She paused with her fingers curled around the top edge of his briefs. "Am I hurting you? Should I stop?"

"No!" His denial was as vehement as hers had been. "Lord, no, don't stop. Don't ever st—" The word ended in another groan as her hand closed around his straining flesh.

He'd never felt so wanted, so passionately desired, in his life! But if he didn't stop her, right now, he'd disgrace himself and leave them both unsatisfied. "Kate. Kate, darlin'." He reached for her hand, intending to remove it, but instead found himself cupping it, curling her hand more firmly around him as he showed her the movement and the pressure he liked best.

"That feels so good," he crooned, lost in the pleasure of her hands on him. A minute more and he'd make her stop. Just a minute more! "So damned good."

Her hips were moving rhythmically, in time to her stroking hand, rotating against his thighs in an unconscious effort to ease the pressure building inside her.

Closer.

Did she say it out loud? Or only think it?

Closer.

"Jesse." It was the whisper of a woman on the edge. "Jesse, please. I need you closer."

"Closer?"

"Inside me."

Died and gone to heaven! He struggled to sit up, twisting an arm around behind him to the nightstand for the protection she'd been so adamant about supplying, wondering if he could steady his hands long enough to get the darned thing open.

She reached out to stop him. "No."

"No?" He looked up at her in confusion. "No what?"

"I don't want anything between us," she said, surprising herself as well as him. But it was true. She didn't want anything between them, not even a thin rubber sheath. Especially not a thin rubber sheath. "Nothing."

"Kate, darlin'," he said, touched and more than a little awed by her passionate ferocity. He didn't want anything between them, either, but one of them had to be sensible. "We can't take the chance you might get pregnant." That was the only thing he was worried about; the other reason for wearing condoms wasn't even a consideration, not with her.

"It's all right. I won't." Pregnancy had been the least of her concerns; she couldn't remember what the others had been. They didn't matter. "I'm on the Pill." She squirmed up his body until the cotton panel of her lace panties was directly over his throbbing male flesh. "Come inside me now," she demanded. Pleaded. "With nothing between us."

He encountered one more barrier as he moved to oblige her. "Your panties," he rasped. "Let me help you get them off."

"Tear them. I don't care," she said when he looked at her for confirmation. Her eyes were almost completely dilated, more black than brown, fierce with her passion. "Tear them."

An extra measure of excitement knifed through him as he curled his fingers around the narrow ribbon of lace riding low on her hip. He tugged experimentally, testing the strength of the fabric. He'd never torn a woman's clothes off before.

"Jesse!"

He yanked hard, and the panties came away in his hand. He felt like whirling them around his head like a trophy, and might have, except for the fact that she moved then, lifting herself to her knees, and reached between them to position him. He dropped the panties and reached for her with both hands, grasping her hips to steady and control her descent. She covered his hands with hers and closed her eyes, anticipating the pleasure of his possession.

He entered her slowly, just a bit at a time, his biceps coiled against the urge to take it fast, his teeth clamped together against the burning pleasure of taking it slow. Sweat broke out on his chest and his upper lip as he struggled to maintain control.

"Closer," Kate said.

There was a smacking sound as their bodies came together.

He groaned like a man mortally wounded.

She moaned like a woman rent in two.

They both sighed in sublime and utter satisfaction. *Fusion.*

For a moment, it was enough. And then his hands tightened on her hips, lifting her, and she leaned forward, reaching out to balance herself on his chest as she moved against him.

"Oh, yes," he breathed, watching her rock above him with her eyes closed and her lush breasts bobbling with her movements. She was a pagan goddess. Essential woman. Temptation incarnate in her frilly, feminine white garter belt and silk stockings. "Oh, yes. Just like that, darlin'. Just exactly like that."

"Jesse." Her long, elegant fingers curled in his damp chest hair. "Oh, Jesse."

"It's okay, darlin'. Just let me have it. Let it go." he reached for the curly auburn hair between her thighs, his fingers searching for her most sensitive flesh.

When he found it, soft and swollen and slippery, she whimpered. "Don't hold back," he coaxed, stroking her. If she held back much longer he wasn't going to make it. "Let me have it all."

Kate threw her head back and let her climax take her. It was the most explosive, most exciting, most terrifying feeling she'd ever experienced. It tightened every muscle in her body until she was as taut as a bowstring, holding her there for an endless aching second, quivering with the strain, and then cast her, limp, exhausted and exhilarated, on her lover's heaving chest.

He held her tight, his arms like bands of steel around her, his body straining, his narrow hips surging upward in one last powerful thrust as he emptied everything he had into her. His love, his life force, everything he was and everything he hoped to become. He was hers in that intensely emotional, blindingly physical moment. Utterly hers, as if there had never been another woman for him and never would be again.

As they lay together in the aftermath, gentling each other with soft, wordless murmurs and softer caresses, he felt a strong, almost overpowering urge to tell her he loved her. And to demand her love in return.

He wasn't sure what stopped him. Ego, maybe. *Ego, probably,* he amended, smiling wryly at the fan that twirled lazily above the bed.

The fact that Kate hadn't said anything about love or given any indication she'd even thought about it was certainly a part of his reluctance to declare himself. The fact that words of love spoken in the throes of passion were often lies or, at best, rosy distortions of the truth was another. But, mostly, it was his remembered feelings of embarrassment, the faint distaste and pity he'd felt for women who'd declared their love for him after just one night together.

Passion, no matter how overwhelming, wasn't love. He knew that. She knew that. If he declared himself now she wouldn't believe him. She'd think that they were just pretty words, polite payment for the surrender of her body.

No, he thought, idly stroking her back with both hands, when he said the words "I love you" he didn't want there to be any doubt in her mind that he meant them. And he wanted, please God, to hear her say them back.

He could wait for the right time. Not long, probably. But he could wait. Especially if she intended to keep him occupied like this while he waited!

Kate snuggled against him, replete and complete and utterly pleased with herself. *I don't have to wonder anymore*, she thought, joyful and relieved and awed, all at the same time. Jesse *was* incredible in bed! And he made her feel incredible! It was a delightful way to feel.

She raised herself up on one elbow, pushing her hair out of her face to look at him.

"What?" he murmured lazily.

She smiled, a siren's smile of self-satisfied femininity. "Why did we wait so long to do this?"

Jesse's lips quirked up in an answering grin. "You can't blame me for that," he drawled. "I was just waiting for you to tell me you were ready."

"Well, I'm ready."

His low laugh was the sexiest sound she'd ever heard. "What, again?"

9

KATE WASN'T QUITE SURE what she expected of the morning after the night before with Jesse. Especially when, on awakening to find herself alone in his bed, she began to wonder if her motives for seducing him weren't as simple as she thought.

Should a woman feel so desolate and deserted upon waking up alone in her lover's bed? And, finding herself alone, should she immediately start worrying about where said lover was and what might have happened to him and if she'd ever feel his arms around her again?

She'd never felt that way with Reed. Of course, she'd never spent a night with Reed like the one she'd spent with Jesse.

It made her blush to think about it.

She'd been...well, the only word that came to mind was wanton. She'd been wanton. And greedy. And demanding.

Too demanding?

And then, no, she thought, not too demanding. Jesse had risen...she giggled and slid down under the rumpled white sheets as if someone were there to watch her blush—Jesse had risen to each and every demand and still had enough energy to make a few demands of his own.

Their second loving had started out slow and easy, with laughter and teasing and tickling. He'd unsnapped her garters and rolled her stockings down her legs, one at a time, pressing soft, teasing kisses down her thighs to her toes and back up again, looking at her through his lashes with that wicked grin of his, pretending he was going to bite her so she'd wiggle and squeal.

When he'd got the stockings off, he rolled her over onto her stomach to unfasten the garter belt. And then he kept her there, gliding his palms over the sleek skin of her back, running the tip of his tongue down her spine, kneading the firm globes of her buttocks, teasing the soft cleft between them with the tip of his finger until she moaned and parted her legs.

He'd accepted the silent invitation with satisfying celerity, curving his fingers into the soft, moist folds of her, searching out and finding all the pleasure points hidden between her silky thighs. By the time he rolled her onto her back, she was flushed and damp and needy. But still he lingered, savoring her with all the care of a gourmet at his last meal, turning the playful loving into a hedonistic, luxurious, voluptuously sensual exploration of her body with his eyes and hands and tongue that left no part of her untouched or unappreciated.

He kissed her face and throat, her shoulders and arms and the tip of each long, elegant finger. He rubbed his face against her breasts and belly and the fleecy auburn hair between her legs. He spoke to her every fantasy and need, his words flowing over her, as thick and sweet as his drawl, as hot as his vivid blue eyes.

Words of praise and appreciation, murmured against her damp skin. Incoherent murmurs of pleasure. Descriptions of what he was going to do to her and how it would make her feel and what it did to him when she cried out at his touch.

When he finally moved to enter her it was almost an act of mercy. She was out of her mind with wanting him, limp and aching, so overcome that she could do no more than lie there with her eyes closed and wait for him to fill her.

He hovered between her splayed legs, his hands cradling her hips. "Open your eyes, darlin'," he coaxed. "Come on. Open those beautiful eyes and look at me when I love you."

Her lashes drifted upward slowly, as if they were too heavy for her lids. Her eyes focused, widening, then narrowing in passionate appraisal of the man kneeling between her thighs.

He was so beautiful it made her heart ache. His tawny hair was tousled and damp with sweat. His blue eyes were blazing, hot enough to burn. His normally smiling mouth was set in the tight lines of desire. The diamond in his left ear glittered, catching the faint light coming in through the long glass doors, telling her, reminding her, somehow, that this was a man different from any man she'd ever known before.

She lifted a languid hand to touch it, wanting to let him know she approved and appreciated that difference. Her fingers landed on his sweat-sheened shoulder. "I like your earring," she murmured.

Jesse's smile was strained through layers of passion. "Only my earring?"

"And your shoulders," she said, rubbing the flat of her hand over his taut trapezius muscle. She let it drift down and then inward. "And your chest," she said, caressing the hard, smooth muscles. "And your hair." Her fingers trailed lazily, languidly through his crinkly gold chest hairs. "Here." Her hand drifted lower. "And here." His stomach muscles twitched under her hand. "And here," she whispered, boldly inching her fingers down to the base of his erection.

He caught her wrist. "You leave that alone." The warning was only half teasing. His slow exploration of her body and her sizzling response to it had left him teetering on the edge of control.

She smiled at him through slitted eyes. "Only if you promise to do something constructive with it."

"Like what?" he purred.

She whispered a two-word instruction that brought him plunging into her and would cause her to blush every time she thought of it for the next week. But not just then.

Just then, all she could think about was him and the way he felt moving in and out of her—so slow and sweet and hard—and how she felt as all the small delicate muscles of her body clenched and flexed to hold him. She undulated like a wave beneath him, receiving and returning his slow thrusts, sinuous as a snake until the moment she stiffened and cried out.

"That's it, darlin'. Sing to me. Tell me how good it feels." His thighs clenched, pressing her into the mattress as his own climax took him. His breath hissed out between his teeth. "It feels real good, doesn't it?"

Kate nodded and held on tight as the lingering little aftershocks of pleasure spiraled through her.

And so now I know what he says in the throes of passion, she thought, feeling the heat sizzle through her even now, the morning after, as she lay in his bed and remembered all the things he'd said. To paraphrase Lilac, Jesse de Vallerin knew just what to say to make a woman feel real good.

Except, Kate thought, the words she suddenly realized she'd been unconsciously waiting to hear.

He hadn't mentioned love.

"Oh, don't be ridiculous," she said aloud, thoroughly annoyed with herself. "You didn't mention love, either."

And she wouldn't. She wasn't in love with Jesse de Vallerin. Infatuated, yes. Besotted, certainly. Smitten, without a doubt. But not in love.

That was just her old, middle-class, Boston-bred values rearing their outdated heads, trying to justify the night she'd just spent in wild sexual abandon with a man she wasn't married to, and had no plans to marry, either. She didn't need to justify the way she'd spent the night, despite what her Hightower conscience tried to tell her. A woman didn't have to be in love to make love. She merely had to . . . to what?

"Have an itch?" Kate asked aloud.

"Would you like me to scratch it for you, darlin'?"

Kate started and looked up to see Jesse standing in the bedroom doorway. She waited for the embarrassment to come, the shyness at what had passed between them in the night and the foolishness she should feel at having been caught talking to herself, but it didn't come.

She felt nothing but pleasure when she looked at Jesse. "Is that breakfast?" she said, gesturing at the white paper sack dangling from his left hand.

"Might be." He came into the room, bringing warmth and life and the rich scent of chicory coffee and sugary beignets with him, and sat on the edge of the bed. "Depends on your answer to my question."

"Which was?" she said archly, reaching for the sack.

He held it away from her. "Whether this itch of yours needs scratching or not."

"And if it does?"

"Then I might be persuaded to feed you first."

"First?"

His grin was positively wicked. "Before I scratch that itch."

They ate the beignets, getting powdered sugar all over the bed and each other, and drank the hot chicory coffee. And then he shed his clothes and crawled into bed with her, and made slow sweet love to her again.

It was a tender loving, the slow-building, low-burning kind of loving that ended with sighs and murmurs and soft, throaty moans instead of shouts and muffled screams. The kind of loving that leaves both lovers sated and sleepy and utterly content with the world and everyone in it.

Kate snuggled into the curve of Jesse's body when it was over, silently congratulating herself on the success of her first seduction and the ease with which she'd handled the morning after. She drifted off to sleep, too satisfied with herself to wonder what Lilac was going to say when her houseguest came dragging home well after breakfast, and didn't wake up until Jesse smacked her on the bottom.

"Crawl out of that bed, you lazy wanton. We're going to a ball game."

THE IMAGES CLIPPERS played a team with the name of a local pizzeria emblazoned on their shirts while Kate sat in the bleachers between Amber, the red-haired cocktail waitress, and Jesse's oldest sister, Aimée, and learned more about her lover than she'd ever have had the nerve to ask but not nearly as much as she wanted to know.

"Feeling better?" Amber asked after Jesse had made sure Kate was settled in her seat.

"Better?" Kate said, wondering why Jesse had had the bad taste to sit one girlfriend next to another.

"The headache?"

"Oh. Yes, much better, thank you."

"That's good." She leaned closer as Jesse jogged off to the bench where his team waited for him. "Brian said Jesse seemed kinda worried about you last Saturday."

"Brian?" Kate mumbled absently, mesmerized by the sight of Jesse surrounded by a dozen or more energetic little boys in burgundy and white uniforms. Little girls she could understand—maybe—but little boys? He was the kind of man who brought out the flirt in every female—young or old—but he hadn't struck her as the kind of man to inspire boyish hero worship. Obviously, she'd been wrong.

"Brian's my son. That's him down there," Amber said proudly. "Number twenty-four." She pointed at a small, red-haired boy who looked to have all the freckles his mother didn't and quite a few of his own besides. "Jesse's his Big Brother and he's been—"

"Big brother?"

"Yeah, you know, that organization that matches up kids who don't have any male influence in their lives with guys like Jesse? Anyway, Jesse's been taking care of him on Saturdays for me for the past couple of months. I've been going to real estate school. I take my test next week." She grinned, suddenly looking a lot like the little boy on the field. "And then it's goodbye Bourbon Street." She waved at a teenager selling peanuts. "Want some?" she asked Kate.

Kate shook her head.

Jesse'd been baby-sitting? Jesse? The man who turned her bones to lava and her brains to mush—*baby-sitting?* She just couldn't picture it. And then again . . . Her gaze wandered to the field.

Amber leaned around her to the woman on Kate's other side. "Aimée?" she said, offering her peanuts.

"Already got popcorn," Jesse's sister said, holding up a paper bag.

Kate sat between them, her wondering gaze resting on the golden, tawny-haired Adonis standing with one hand on his lean, blue-jeaned hip and the other on the shoulder of a young ballplayer.

"So, you're from Boston."

Reluctantly, Kate gave her attention to the Adonis's sister. "Yes, I am."

"And how are you liking New Orleans?"

"It's lovely."

"Yes, it is, isn't it? I've lived here all my life and—" She broke off, surging to her feet as the crack of the bat signaled a possible home run. She sat down almost immediately when the high fly was miraculously caught by the center fielder on the other team. "So, how long have you known my brother?"

"I, ah . . ." Kate's eyes remained fixed on the field, watching as Jesse swooped down on the crestfallen player who'd had his potential home run grabbed out of the air. He scooped the boy up as he trudged to the bench and hugged him, whispering something into his ear. The child shrugged and finally nodded. He was smiling when Jesse set him on his feet and headed him toward the rest of his team.

It was then, at that precise instant, that Kate realized what she felt for Jesse de Vallerin was more than just an intense physical attraction and fondness. It was an unsettling thought, coming as it did on the heels of the uneasiness she'd felt this morning when she woke in an empty bed.

"Miz Hightower?" Aimée prodded delicately.

"Call me Kate, please," she said, trying to look interested as she turned toward the woman sitting beside her. It wasn't easy when her whole concept of the world was undergoing serious reviewing. But she tried.

Aimée Butterfield had the same tawny blond hair and blue eyes as her brother and much of the same sweetness in her smile—when she smiled. Right now, she looked like a teaching nun bent on interrogation.

"I'm sorry," Kate said, instantly contrite. "What did you ask me?"

"I was just wondering how long you've known my brother."

"About . . ." *How long has it been?* "A little over a week." *Amazing.* "We met through Lilac Prescott," she added, anticipating the next question. North or South, families were families; they all wanted credentials when a stranger became involved with one of their own. "Lilac and I were at Radcliffe together."

Jesse's sister smiled. "Ah, yes, Lilac," she said, glancing at the action on the field as another batter sent the ball sailing over the pitcher's head. "I haven't seen her for ages. How's she doing with that new store of hers?"

"Just fine," Kate said. "I've been helping her—"

The women on either side of her jumped to their feet with identical screams of rage.

"Kill the ump!" Aimée hollered, using her cupped hands to magnify the sound.

"Give it to him, Jesse!" Amber screamed encouragingly.

Kate looked at the field to see Jesse—slow-moving, sweet-talking, easy-going Jesse—surrounded by a gang of bouncing, hollering, wildly excited kids, standing toe-to-toe with the umpire. There was some theatrical hand-waving and finger-pointing and then a cheer went up as Jesse obviously made his point. He leaned over, picking his baseball cap off the ground where he'd thrown it when things got heated, and shepherded his charges to their bench.

Kate felt that awareness of something other than physical attraction and fondness grow by a few critical degrees. A man whose kisses could melt steel was dangerous enough when it came to a woman's good sense. Add the ability to make children adore him— as these children so obviously did—and he became positively lethal.

"Jesse has to watch that jerk umpire like a hawk," Aimée said as she plopped down in her seat. "He's always calling the girls out when they're not."

"Girls?" Kate mumbled, still dwelling on the power of Jesse's kisses combined with the possible implications of his Pied Piper tendencies.

Aimée pointed to the sidelines just as Jesse opened his arms to catch the wily body that hurled itself at him for a victory hug. A long dark blond braid tumbled down the burgundy jersey as the player's hat came off.

"My daughter Laura," Aimée said. "She just made the tying run."

Kate tried but she didn't get any more information out of either woman after that. Laura Butterfield's run had brought the score to three even, and it wasn't until the last half of the last inning that either mother had any attention left over for the woman sitting between them.

"Well, I'm glad that's over," said Aimée, standing as the Clippers' seventh and winning run was batted in by a sacrifice fly.

"Have Jesse bring you by the club again," Amber said before heading off to gather up her son. "I'll be working there for a couple more weeks at least."

Kate nodded and said she'd mention it to Jesse.

"These things always turn me into a nervous wreck," said Jesse's sister. She linked her arm through Kate's as they descended the bleachers. "We're having a little family birthday party for Laura tomorrow afternoon after church," Aimée Butterfield said as they walked to the Clippers' bench to join Jesse and his cheering team of pint-size ball players. "We'd love to have you come with Jesse if you're still in town."

THE NEXT AFTERNOON, despite her protests that she really didn't belong at an intimate family gathering, Kate found herself attending Laura Butterfield's ninth birthday party. The minute they walked through the front door of the Louisiana-style Victorian, they were surrounded by what seemed to be a half-dozen children, all clamoring for their Uncle Jesse's attention.

It didn't take much in the way of deductive reasoning to figure out where he'd gotten his experience feeding babies, Kate thought, hanging back a bit as she watched the noisy group welcome their uncle. His sisters obviously kept him well-supplied with nephews and nieces, all of whom looked remarkably like him, each other and their mothers, making assigning a particular child to any one female parent impossible.

"Look at me, Uncle Jethee, look at me!" lisped a tiny child in a pink tutu and sneakers as she pirouetted around them.

"Well, aren't you a pretty little princess," her uncle Jesse said admiringly.

"Hey, Uncle Jesse." A gangly boy of about thirteen held up his hand for a high five.

"Hey, Robert," Jesse said, obliging him.

"I want long nails for the sixth grade dance, Uncle Jesse," said a preteen belle in strategically tattered blue jeans and a ruffled blouse. "Tell Mama I'm old enough to have artificial nails." She shot a disgruntled glance over her shoulder at the adults gathered in the living room awaiting their turn to greet the favorite son while waving the hand on which she'd inexpertly applied a set of inch-long, dime-store fingernails under Jesse's nose for his inspection. Her other arm was wrapped around a drooling baby of indeterminate sex with its hands fisted in her pale blond hair.

Jesse studied her handiwork with appropriate seriousness. "How 'bout you come on in and let Didi give you a French manicure for the dance, darlin'?" he suggested, reaching out to chuck the baby under the chin. "It's the latest thing."

"Great!" She transferred the baby to her uncle Jesse's arms. "I'll go tell Mama."

"Uncle Jesse, you came!" screeched the birthday girl as she hurtled into the crowded foyer.

"Take Jessica here, would you, darlin'?" Jesse handed the baby to Kate and held out his arms, catching Laura as she launched herself at him for a hug. "Of course I came, Slugger. Did you think I wouldn't?"

"I heard Mama tell Aunt Ginny that you had a new girlfriend." She looked over at Kate. "I wasn't sure you'd come if you had a new girlfriend."

"Well, I did." He kissed the child and set her on her feet. "This is Katherine Hightower." He put his arm around her, baby and all, and brought her forward. "She's a Yankee from up Boston way," he said, echoing the words he'd used to introduce her to the snowball man on their first date. "If you're all real nice she might decide she likes New Orleans and stay awhile."

"She's pretty, Uncle Jesse," the sneakered ballerina proclaimed. "I didn't know Yankees were so pretty."

"Oh, don't be a stoop, Carey Lyn," Laura admonished her younger cousin with another considering look at Kate. "Uncle Jesse's girlfriends are always pretty."

"Go on out to the porch, all of you, now." Aimée Butterfield ordered, clapping her hands at the kids as she came into the foyer. "We'll have cake in a few minutes."

She reached out and took the baby from Kate's arms, expertly untangling the tiny hand from the thin gold chain Kate wore around her neck without doing either of them any damage. "Jessica's at the stage where she wants to put everything in her mouth," she explained, and Kate realized it wasn't Aimée at all but another one of Jesse's sisters.

"I'm Chantal," she said, her warm smile doing nothing to hide the careful scrutiny she was giving her brother's guest. It was very much like the look Laura had given her. "Come in and meet everyone."

"ARE ALL YOUR GIRLFRIENDS really pretty?" Kate said later, when she and Jesse were laying in his bed beneath the slowly twirling ceiling fan, sated and damp from a rousing bout of lovemaking.

He rolled onto his elbow and looked at her. She was his only girlfriend—such an insipid word for all the things she was to him!—and she was so pretty it made him ache. "Yep," he said, reaching out to brush a strand of hair off her cheek. "You jealous?"

"No more than you are of my boyfriends," she lied, not knowing how true the statement was.

Jesse's eyes darkened. "Let's not talk about old lovers," he said, bending his head to start their lovemaking all over again.

10

THE NEXT AFTERNOON, before she went to Lilac's shop, Kate had to be content with a quick lunch at a small, homey café halfway between Images and Secrets because, Jesse explained with a grin, a man had to work sometime. She spent the rest of the day working at Lilac's shop.

"Actually, I'm glad to see some evidence that he views his career with the proper respect," Kate said to her friend.

Lilac looked up from the display rack they were fitting together. "What kind of crack is that?"

"I just meant that he seems to spend a lot of time away from that salon of his, that's all," Kate defended herself, guilty about all the time she was spending away from Hightower Charities. Of course, if she hadn't fled Boston, she'd be on her honeymoon now, but still... The ingrained habits of a lifetime were hard to shake. "He'll never get ahead that way."

"Don't you worry about Jesse gettin' ahead," Lilac admonished. "He's one man who's exactly where he wants to be."

"Which is?" Kate prodded, trying to pump Lilac for information without seeming to. Her growing interest in everything about Jesse de Vallerin was too new, too tentative and too unsettling to risk exposing it to Lilac's teasing, no matter how good-natured and well-intended. As it was, she could only be thankful her temporary roommate realized that her new physical relationship was off-limits for teasing, too.

"Happy with who and what he is," Lilac said. "Work isn't the be-all and end-all of Jesse's life. I'd think you'd know that by now—"

Yes, Kate thought, *I know.*

"—but he does just fine. He owns two other salons, you know."

No, she hadn't known that. Jesse didn't talk much about his business except to say he loved it. And that much was obvious without him having to say it.

"He owns them lock, stock and barrel, too—" Lilac nodded emphatically "—including the one here in the Quarter."

"Really?" Kate murmured encouragingly. She found it hard to imagine the laid-back man she knew hustling enough to keep one business going, let alone three. And yet, there was that side of him she'd seen on the baseball field. *That* man had been anything but laid-back. Maybe Lilac was about to reveal another facet of his personality.

"He's got a salon over in Baton Rouge that caters to the L.S.U. crowd," Lilac said, "and one in Metairie. It was his first one, actually." She pounded the last piece of antiqued brass tubing into place with the flat of her hand as she spoke. "It's just an itty-bitty place. Nothin' like the other two," she said, stepping back to judge the effect of the finished display rack. "I think he probably hangs on to it for sentimental reasons. Not that it isn't profitable," she said, anticipating Kate's comment on the wisdom of hanging onto any business for sentimental value alone; as a Yankee and a Hightower, she had a built-in aversion to letting emotion cloud good business judgment. "Jesse's always been real handy at turnin' a profit," she said admiringly. "He's had to be."

Kate handed her a piece of the next display rack before she could reach for it. "Had to be?" she asked.

"Uh-huh. He was only nine when his daddy died. Heart attack, I think. Anyway, there wasn't any money in the family," she said, head bent as she fit two lengths of tubing together. "He didn't leave any insurance money, or not much, from what I remember my Mama sayin' at the time, and Miz de Vallerin had to go out to work. Not havin' any kind of trainin' or anythin' she took a job in a little beauty shop, shampooin' hair. It was real hard for a while there." She shrugged sympathetically. "Well, you can imagine. What with four little kids for her to feed and clothe and one of them bein' just a baby when it happened."

Kate found it hard to imagine Jesse's mother, the lovely, laughing woman she'd met yesterday at Laura's birthday party, being in the position Lilac described.

She'd looked carefree and cared for, as if she'd never known a day's hard work or a moment's worry in her life, and at least ten years too young to be the mother of four grown children and the grandmother of seven.

"Anyway, to make a long story short," Lilac said. "Jesse hated for his mama to have to work like that, even after she was promoted to receptionist. Hand me that piece there, would you, honey?"

Kate handed her the length of antiqued brass without a word, amazed at all she was learning about the closemouthed Jesse. He'd never said anything at all about this part of his life! Never mentioned the hardships that must have preceded the relative luxury he now enjoyed. Kate had assumed, quite naturally, she thought, that there must be money in his family and that Images was just some sort of hobby with him. It wasn't true, obviously. So why had he let her go on thinking he was nothing more than a feckless charmer?

"He went to work at the same beauty shop almost at the same time his mama did, as near as I can recall," Lilac said. "Swept floors, ran errands for the customers, things like that. He was always a real favorite with the ladies, even as a little boy."

Kate didn't doubt that for a minute.

"He's been in the business, one way or another, ever since," Lilac rambled on. "And it's been real good to him. He helped put all three of his sisters through college, even though he never did get to go himself, and bought his mama a little shotgun house over on Prytania as soon as he could afford it. She doesn't live in it anymore, not since she up and married that shipping tycoon a couple of years ago, but Jesse still owns it. Along with I don't know what else."

Kate felt another layer of emotion settle into place as she listened to the abbreviated story of Jesse's life. Compassion for the child he'd been. Admiration for the man he'd become. Appropriate emotions, she told herself, given what she'd just learned about him. Entirely appropriate, and yet . . .

Why did she suddenly feel all weepy and so tenderly proud, like a mother whose child had done something selfless and brave? And why did her heart feel as if it had turned over in her breast? And why, oh why, was she suddenly so afraid of whatever emotion was churning around inside her?

But she knew why.

An affair—and that's what she shared with Jesse, she told herself, just an affair—with a man who could be dismissed as merely a gorgeous hunk with an engaging personality was one thing; easily understood, easily indulged in, and just as easily forgotten. An affair with a gorgeous hunk who cared about children and who adored—and was obviously adored by—his family was a bit more complicated but still manageable if a woman kept her head and didn't allow herself to get too deeply involved. But an affair with a gorgeous hunk who'd been blessed with a sexy, engaging personality, an affinity for children and family *and* a sterling character...ah, now that was a man who could make you fall in love whether you thought you wanted to or not.

The thing was...had she fallen in love without knowing it?

SHE WAS IN THE STOREROOM, steaming the wrinkles out of a shipment of fancy silk robes, still wondering more or less the same thing, when she thought she heard the little bell over the front door jingle. Secrets wasn't officially open yet, but people had been coming in and out all day. Friends of Lilac's, mostly, to say hi and see how things were going, neighboring retailers dropping by to check out the competition, delivery men with another of the orders that had been arriving steadily for the last couple of days and, now and then, a prospective customer who'd ignored the closed sign and come in anyway. They'd already made three unexpected sales that way.

The bell could also have signaled the arrival of Jesse, whom she was expecting to take her out to dinner after Images closed for the day, or Lilac, who'd run out to do a few errands.

"Lilac?" she called hopefully. She wasn't quite ready to see Jesse again, not until she decided exactly what she was going to say to him—or what she would do if the most wonderful, earth-shattering thing that had ever happened to her turned out to be of minor importance to him. "Lilac, is that you?"

There was no answer.

Kate shut the steamer off and went to see if anyone had come in. Lilac, she thought, was going to have to invest in a new bell. Pretty as it was, the one she had wasn't really loud enough to be heard in the back room.

But she'd heard right this time, someone had come in.

A tall, stately woman stood with her back to Kate, fingering a richly colored, extravagantly fringed paisley silk shawl that had been draped over the open door of a satiny cherry-wood armoire as a backdrop for a pearl-pink chemise on a padded satin hanger. A dozen other chemises, twins to the one on display in everything except color, and half a dozen different styles of camisoles and teddies, hung inside the armoire. A pair of feathered white mules lay on the floor in front of it. The effect was that of a lady's closet, momentarily left open while she went off to do something else. It was her first attempt at creating a display, and Kate was quite pleased with it.

Something about the board-straight back in front of her told Kate the unknown woman wasn't pleased at all.

Probably not a customer, then, she thought. And almost certainly not a neighboring retailer; her tweedy blue suit was too formal for the Quarter. One of Lilac's horde of relatives, maybe? There were one or two elderly, old-fashioned second cousins twice removed who, Lilac had explained, deplored the thought of a Prescott selling women's underclothes.

Kate cleared her throat. "Excuse me," she said politely, wishing Lilac were here to deal with her disapproving relatives. Kate didn't really feel up to dealing with anything except her nagging fears about Jesse's possible reaction to her declaration of love. "May I help you?"

The woman turned. "I certainly hope you may, young woman," she intoned, looking down her nose at Kate.

Not one of Lilac's relatives.

One of hers.

Here.

In New Orleans.

In Lilac's lingerie shop.

The last time her great-aunt had left Boston on an unscheduled trip was ... Kate couldn't remember when the last time was. Not in her lifetime, certainly. Katherine Hightower the elder considered Boston to be the center of the civilized world, if not the entire universe, and only deigned to go beyond the city limits for her regular quarterly trips to New York and a yearly two weeks spent in whatever European country she'd decided, well in advance, to tour. That she was now outside the much-vaunted limits of Boston, unscheduled, boded no good for Katherine Hightower the younger.

"Oh, my God."

"There's no need to take our Lord's name in vain, Katherine."

"Yes, ma'am." The quick spurt of guilt was automatic; her great-aunt had always had the ability to make her feel like a badly behaved child, even when her conscience was clear. "Sorry," she said, wondering if three nights of uninhibited sex—and one afternoon quickie—showed in a person's face.

"And don't mumble," the older woman ordered. "It only annoys people."

"Yes, ma'am."

"Well," she demanded. "Are you going to ask me to sit down, or must I continue to stand?"

"Yes, of course. Sit down. No, wait, the settee won't be delivered until tomorrow." There was going to be a pale gray velvet settee and two delicate lilac brocade chairs to add to the intimate boudoir feel of Secrets. "There's a couple of chairs in the back room," she offered. "We could sit down in there, if you like."

Katherine Hightower inclined her head regally.

"It's a little messy," Kate said, leading the way. *Understatement of the year.* "We only finished the painting a few days ago and we're just starting to get all the stock unpacked." She snatched a haphazard pile of boxes off a folding chair. "Have a seat," she

said, looking around her for a place to put them
down.

The elder Katherine sniffed disdainfully and
waited.

Her niece reached out and brushed off the seat with
her hand. "There, how's that?"

Her great-aunt deigned to sit. She placed her ancient, meticulously cared for leather Chanel bag on
her lap and folded her veined, age-spotted hands on
top of it with the air of an old and powerful queen
waiting to pass sentence on some hapless minion. Kate
quickly found a place for the pile of boxes and dragged
another chair over for herself.

Katherine Hightower fixed her great-niece with a
steely, eagle-eyed gaze. "What on earth have you done
to yourself?" she demanded.

Kate lifted her hand to the front of her pastel floral
cotton jacket. The dress underneath was brand new,
pale peach and strapless, meant to showcase her
magnificent bosom for Jesse's entertainment and ed-
ification later that night. "I, ah..." She lifted her hand
to her unbound hair, acutely aware of how wild and
frizzled it must look. Jesse loved it that way; it would
appall her great-aunt. "I had my hair cut."

Katherine Hightower shook her head disapprovingly. "I assume this transformation—" she sniffed at
the word "—is all part of this nonsense you're indulging in?"

"What nonsense is that, Aunt Katherine?" Kate asked with feigned calm, telling herself not to get upset over her great-aunt's interference. Getting upset only prolonged the process because there was nothing the elder Katherine enjoyed more than upsetting people. Except, perhaps, browbeating them into submission. It was, as she'd said more than once, her only amusement these days.

"You've behaved in a deplorable fashion, young woman." She fixed Kate with a steely gaze from eyes that were remarkably similar to the younger woman's. "Deplorable and highly irresponsible. Your mother is in a tizzy, trying to pretend nothing out of the ordinary has happened." She flicked her hand disdainfully; Frances Hightower was always in a tizzy about something. "And young Edward—" young Edward was Kate's fifty-eight-year-old father "—is hiding out in his office until you come to your senses."

Or until you tire of haranguing him about his latest shortcomings as a father, Kate thought.

"And as for that fiancé of yours..."

Ex-fiancé.

"Well, it pains me to say it, but I'm beginning to think he's more than you deserve."

Much more, Kate agreed silently.

"I hope you realize how lucky you are, Katherine, to have a man like Reed Sullivan ready and waiting to marry you after the deplorable way you've behaved."

Except that I don't want a man like Reed.

"He's showing a great deal more understanding than I would under the circumstances."

Or any other, when things aren't to your liking, you old harridan.

"Katherine! Are you listening to me?"

"Yes, Aunt Katherine." *And listening...and listening...* She had been listening to her great-aunt and the rest of her relatives for most of her life. It was past time she started listening to herself.

"Well?"

She tried a small, placating smile. "Well, what?"

"Don't pretend you don't know what I mean, young woman," Katherine Hightower snapped.

Kate's smile faded; rebellion was easier long-distance.

"Are you going to stop this nonsense and come home where you belong?"

Well, that depends, Kate thought, *on a lot of things.* Not the least of which was Jesse de Vallerin's reaction to having her declare her undying love.

"Katherine!"

Kate took a deep breath and finally asserted her long-overdue independence. "No, I don't think so, Aunt Katherine," she said softly but very firmly. "Not anytime soon, anyway. And not ever to marry Reed."

"And just why not, may I ask?" Katherine demanded, as insulted as if Kate had rejected her personally; Reed Sullivan, after all, was her hand-picked choice for her favorite niece and namesake.

"Because I finally realized he's not in love with me and I—"

"Nonsense! Reed's very fond of you."

"I'm fond of him, too," Kate admitted, "but I'm *not* in love with him."

"You picked a fine time for all these realizations of yours, I must say," Katherine huffed. She eyed her great-niece with sudden speculation. "Are you in love with someone else?"

Neither of them heard the merry little jingle over the door announce that someone had entered the shop. Jesse, about to call out and announce his presence, stood stock-still when he heard the question and waited for Kate's answer with as much interest and attention as her great-aunt did. *Yes, Kate, tell us,* he thought. *Are you in love with someone else? Me, for instance?*

Kate took another very deep breath. "No," she said, even as the image of Jesse formed in her mind's eye. She justified the lie by telling herself that whether she was in love with anyone else or not had nothing to do with why she wasn't marrying Reed. "And I don't really think it's any of your business, anyway, Aunt Katherine."

"Well, I never!" Katherine said.

No, Kate thought, *I don't suppose you have.*

*And that's what you get for eavesdropping, de Val-
lerin,* Jesse thought, his heart sinking down to the toes
of his white sneakers. *She isn't in love with someone
else. Least of all you.*

He wondered dismally if he should just throw the
ring he'd been carrying around in his pocket for the
past two days into the Mississippi River and forget the
whole thing.

"At least, I don't think—" Kate shook her head. No,
telling her great-aunt about Jesse at this point would
only send her into apoplexy.

Neither her lover nor her aunt missed the doubt in
Kate's voice. It filled both of them with renewed hope,
although for vastly different reasons. Jesse decided not
to fling the ring into the river, after all. Not until he
knew for sure that Kate wouldn't be wearing it.

"You don't think what?" her great-aunt demanded.
"That you're in love with someone else? Or that you
aren't?"

She was saved from answering by the sound of Lilac's voice raised in greeting. "Why, Jesse, honey, what
are you doin' lurkin' in here among all these ladies'
undies by your lonesome?"

Jesse? Kate thought. *Jesse was in the shop?*

"Lord, woman, you nearly scared me out of a year's
growth." His familiar drawl drifted through the open
door into the back room, sending a thrill through the
woman who'd been both dreading and dying to see
him. "I thought you and Kate were in the store-

room," he lied smoothly. "I could hear voices but nobody answered when I came in."

"Kate's there by herself. Or she was when I left. Kate, honey?" Lilac's voice rose to carry to the back room. "You here?"

"Yes." Kate came to her feet in a rush. "Yes, I'm here."

"Well, good, 'cause I've got a surprise for you. Jesse's—" Lilac came to a stop in the doorway, her bright, teasing smile freezing on her face at the sight of Kate's great-aunt Katherine. Her quick glance at Kate was that of a conspirator who'd inadvertently let the cat out of the bag. "—here," she finished.

There was a moment of highly charged silence as the three women looked at each other. Apprehension and guilty pleasure flickered in one pair of eyes. Speculation and imminent demand glittered in a second. Quick apology sparked a third. Wary consideration tempered all three.

"And just who," Katherine Hightower demanded, "is this Jesse person?"

"I am." Jesse cupped his hands under Lilac's elbows, gently moving her out of his way as he came through the door. "Jesse de Vallerin," he said, advancing on Kate's great-aunt with his usual looselimbed, feline grace and a warmly disarming, effortlessly charming smile on his face.

Kate sucked in her breath. Laid-back, easy-going Jesse, in his faded jeans and his pink Images T-shirt and a white linen jacket covering his lean, elegant frame, with his diamond earring peeking out beneath the tawny strands of his too-long hair and with his sensual charm, was no match for the steel-spined conventionality and tart tongue of the eldest living Hightower. Great-Aunt Katherine wasn't impressed by sex appeal and charm. One wrong word and she'd annihilate him with the sharp side of her tongue. Of the four of them, only Jesse seemed not to know it.

Kate almost reached out to stop him and then changed her mind. *No*, she thought, *he has to learn about Great-Aunt Katherine sooner or later*. She felt like a mother watching her child cross the street for the first time.

"I'm a friend of Kate's. And Lilac's, too, of course," he said, bending to take Katherine's hand in both of his as smoothly as if she'd actually offered it to him. No one looking at him saw the hint of anger and hurt feelings in his blue eyes at the guilt and doubt that had been so evident in Kate's. "And you must be kin to Kate." His smile was as lazily, sweetly charming as if the regally disapproving old woman were a normal, susceptible female and not the terror of the Hightower clan. "You have the same melted-chocolate eyes and creamy skin," he said, meaning it sincerely. The resemblance between Kate and her aristocratic relative was a strong one. "Uncommon beauty must run in the family."

Kate's great-aunt condescended to leave her hand in his for the moment. "Do you expect me to fall for that line?" she asked tartly.

Jesse grinned at her, unabashed by her acerbic tone. "Definitely Kate's kin," he said approvingly.

Katherine Hightower allowed a small smile to curve her lips. "And you, young man, are definitely a rogue."

Kate Hightower nearly swallowed her tongue.

The older woman tilted her head consideringly, almost but not quite flirtatiously, as she looked into Jesse's smiling face. "A charming devil of a rogue," she added, further astonishing her great-niece. She tsked and shook her head. "But still a rogue," she said disapprovingly.

Jesse laughed and, with the unselfconscious grace of a true courtier, raised the old woman's soft, veined hand to his lips. "Why, thank you most kindly, Miz—" He turned to look over his shoulder at the woman who'd doubted him. "Aren't you going to introduce me to this charming lady, Katie, darlin'?"

"I HOPE YOU'RE NOT going to make a fool of yourself over that young man," Katherine Hightower said as she walked down the narrow street with her arm through Kate's after having dismissed Jesse's gallant offer to procure her a taxi.

"My hotel is only a few blocks away," she'd said irritably —she was always irritable when she didn't get her way. "And the walk will do us both good. Besides, I want to talk to Kate. Alone," she added, before Jesse could offer to accompany them. "Well?" she demanded now, when Kate remained silent.

"Well, what, Aunt Katherine?"

"Are you making a fool of yourself over that young man?"

Kate's glance didn't quite meet the older woman's. "Fool?" she said carefully, but she knew what her great-aunt was getting at. She'd been hoping pretty much the same thing—that she wasn't about to make a fool of herself over Jesse de Vallerin.

"He's very charming," Katherine Hightower admitted graciously, "and he has a certain . . . appeal," she added delicately, "that even I, at my advanced age, am quite aware of." She sighed. "One can't help but be aware of it, with that kind of man."

"Which is?" Kate asked, intrigued in spite of herself. Encouraging her great-aunt to air her opinions wasn't something she usually did, but this was a side of the elder Katherine she'd never seen before. Who'd have thought, she marveled, that the oldest living Hightower had a soft spot for . . . What was it she'd called Jesse?

"Rogues," the elder Katherine said succinctly. "Though I suppose they're called something else these days. Well, whatever—" she flicked one hand in a dismissive gesture " —it doesn't matter what they're called, or how charming they are. They're dangerous men as far as women are concerned."

"Dangerous?" Kate said but she knew, very well, what her great-aunt was getting at. She'd known Jesse was dangerous the first time she laid eyes on him.

"You must be very careful not to surrender your heart to him, Katherine." She gave her niece a very sharp, very knowing look. "Whatever else you may have already surrendered."

Kate flushed guiltily. "Aunt Katherine, really!"

"Don't 'Aunt Katherine' me," the older woman said sternly. "I may be an old lady but I'm a long way from being senile. I know what goes on these days." She sniffed delicately. "It's no different from what's always gone on except that women don't have to go around pretending they don't know what's what anymore." She gave another disgruntled sniff. "Not that most of them still don't have a clue. And that includes you."

"Aunt Katherine, I hardly think—"

Katherine Hightower waved her niece to silence. "No, I came down here to see what was going on and have my say and, now that I've seen, well . . . I'll say it just once and then I'll leave it alone."

And pigs will fly, Kate thought.

"Men like Jesse de Vallerin aren't for marrying, Katherine, not for women like you," she said seriously. "And even if you could get him to the altar— which I doubt—he'd end up breaking your heart before you'd been married a year. Men like him are too irresistible to too many women to make good husbands."

"Did it ever occur to you that I might not be interested in marriage, either?" Kate said, wondering why the lie didn't stick in her throat. "I just got rid of one fiancé and—"

"I know you *think* you haven't got marriage on your mind. And maybe you don't. If that's the case, well, then, I suggest you get whatever you do have in mind out of your system as quickly as possible," she said stiffly, "and come back to Boston where you belong. Reed won't wait forever."

"I don't want him to wait at all."

"You think that now but you'll think quite differently when you come to your senses, I assure you," Katherine Hightower said tartly. "When all this ... nonsense is out of your system, you'll be more than happy to have Reed waiting in the wings. He's not got Jesse de Vallerin's roguish ways, I'll grant you, but that's all for the best. He'll provide you with a nice, steady, safe life. The kind of life you're used to."

"And what if I don't want a safe life, Aunt Katherine?" Kate said in exasperation, stopping in the middle of the sidewalk to face her great-aunt. "Did you ever think of that? Did you ever even wonder why I ran out on my wedding rehearsal the way I did?"

"Wedding jitters," Katherine said firmly.

"It was panic," Kate said, throwing her hands up in frustration. "Sheer, unadulterated panic! I suddenly realized if I married Reed nothing . . . *nothing*," she repeated, "would ever change."

"There's no need to shout at me, young woman."

"I'm not shouting," she said, but she lowered her voice anyway; people were staring. "I'm trying to explain."

"Yes, well . . . it isn't me you should be explaining to, it's your fiancé."

"Reed isn't my fiancé!" she said fiercely. "And I have explained it to him but he doesn't listen any better than you— Aunt Katherine?" she said suspiciously. For the first time in memory, Katherine Hightower wasn't meeting her niece's eyes. "What have you done?"

"Nothing that didn't have to be done," the old woman said firmly. "Reed's waiting at the hotel to take you home."

11

"I FEEL REALLY AWFUL about this, Jesse," Kate said into the telephone in Reed Sullivan's hotel room, "but Aunt Katherine's retreated to her room with a fit of the vapors or something—" as transparent a case of interfering matchmaking as Kate had ever seen "—and Reed's kind of at loose ends."

"I understand," Jesse said, his voice carefully unemotional. But he didn't really; not when he remembered the look he'd seen in her big brown eyes when he'd approached her great-aunt Katherine. There'd been doubt in those eyes. And guilt. It made him wonder if he might be wrong about how she was coming to feel about him. A woman in love shouldn't be ashamed of the man she was in love with. *If* she was in love with him.

"He did come all the way down here just to see me," Kate said.

And to take his errant fiancée back to Boston, maybe?

"And we really should talk."

Yeah, I'll bet. Talk. No man chased a woman across state lines just to talk.

"I mean, I do owe him an explanation after everything that's happened."

And what about me? Jesse thought savagely, amazed at the surge of primitive male feelings coursing through him. *What do you owe me, Kate?*

"Jesse?"

"Don't worry about me," Jesse said, trying to sound as if he wasn't seething with jealousy. "I'll find some way to amuse myself while you're busy. Lilac'll take pity on me." His voice faded a bit as he turned away from the phone. "Won't you, darlin'?" he said to Lilac.

Kate heard her friend's laughing agreement drift through the receiver.

"See, there?" Jesse said. "You go on and enjoy yourself."

"Well, okay," she said hesitantly, wondering why he sounded so strange, so cavalier. Did she mean so little to him that he didn't care that she wouldn't be able to have dinner with him tonight? That she was having dinner with her ex-fiancé, instead? "Well," she said again, not knowing what else to say. "Bye, Jesse. See you tomorrow?"

"Bye, darlin'," he said, and, very carefully, to avoid slamming it into the cradle, hung up the receiver.

Kate hung up, too, and stood staring at the phone with a perplexed look on her face. How could a man make love to a woman as if she were the only woman in the world one night and then be totally unconcerned when she went out with her ex-fiancé the next? Wouldn't he be just a little bit jealous? Not, of course, that there was anything for him to be jealous about, but some show of male territoriality wouldn't have been completely inappropriate. If nothing else, it would have shown her that he cared for her more than as just a temporary bedmate. *If* he cared.

Oh, he cares, some more rational part of her mind insisted. A man didn't take a woman to meet his family if he didn't care. But did he care enough?

It certainly didn't feel like it at the moment.

Kate heard the hotel room door open. "Your aunt will be fine," Reed said, closing the door behind him. "I think it's probably just the trip and the heat that's got her down. I ordered her a light supper and she— Kate? Is everything all right?"

Kate turned to face her ex-fiancé, studying him as if she'd never seen him before. He was taller than her by five inches, taller than Jesse by about two. He was lean and well-built, kept in shape by twice weekly tennis matches and a health club membership. His hair was light brown and stylishly—but not too stylishly—cut, with a few distinguished gray threads at the temples. His eyes were blue, his nose straight, his chin square and quite manly. He had a charming smile, lovely manners and the enviable knack of keeping his crisp white shirt, striped tie and medium blue suit as impeccably fresh after a long airplane flight as they'd been when he put them on that morning.

All in all, a very attractive man.

And he moved her not a whit.

He never had, she realized. Not even when she was lying beneath him in bed. She suspected that she'd never moved him much, either, not the way a woman was supposed to move the man she was going to marry. It was nothing short of amazing, really, that they'd ever managed to get into bed together at all. It certainly wasn't desire that had driven them there. She wondered what had.

"Kate?" Reed said again. "Is everything all right?"

"Will you tell me the truth if I ask you something?" she asked, ignoring his question to ask one of her own.

He smiled his charming smile. "I've never lied to you, Kate."

"No? Well..." She shrugged. "Why did you ask me to marry you?" There was nothing but simple curiosity in her eyes as she waited for his answer.

He hesitated a moment. "Truthfully?" he said.

She nodded. "Truthfully."

"Probably for the same reasons you said yes when I asked you. Familiarity. Friendship." He spread his hands. "Because it seemed like the right thing to do. I'm very fond of you, Kate. We have the same tastes, the same interests, the same background. I know what to expect from you." He smiled. "Or, at least, I used to."

"But you don't love me."

"I wanted to love you."

"But you don't."

"No." He shook his head. "For a long time, I thought I did. And then you left me all but standing at the altar and instead of feeling miserable I felt . . . I don't know."

"Free? Relieved?"

"Yes," he agreed. "Relieved."

Kate frowned, wanting to believe him but not quite able to. "If you don't love me," she said carefully, "why did you come after me?"

"You know as well as I do how, ah, persuasive your aunt can be."

"What'd she threaten you with?"

"Nothing outright," Reed said, "but I believe a heart attack in my office was alluded to."

Kate grinned. "Well, whatever the reason, I'm glad you came," she said. "I'm glad we got this whole thing straightened out. It makes me feel a lot better to know I haven't hurt you." She held out her hand. "Friends?" she said.

Reed took her hand in his. "Friends," he agreed and then, briskly, he released it. "Now that that's settled—would you still like to have dinner?"

"Why not?" Kate said. She wasn't having dinner with anyone else tonight.

"Good. Just give me fifteen minutes to shower and change and then you can show me some terrific little restaurant you've found," Reed said, moving toward the bathroom as he spoke. "Call down to room service, why don't you, and order up a pitcher of martinis. We can have a drink on the balcony before we go."

Kate did as he asked, ordering a martini for him and a Pernod for herself, then opened the glass-paned doors leading out to the balcony. Slipping off her light jacket, she tossed it carelessly over the back of one of the wrought-iron chairs and went to stare out over the street below. Her hands on the railing, her head back as she savored the caress of the warm air on her bare shoulders, Kate sighed. In less than one week—and quite aside from the way she felt about Jesse—she'd come to love New Orleans, the sights, the smells, the sounds, the unhurried way life strolled along in the lazy heat.

The sun was just setting, bathing the Quarter in the pink-tinged, golden glow of a summer evening. The air was warm and humid, heavy with the fragrance of the jasmine growing in long narrow troughs around the base of the balcony railing and the scent of the Mississippi in the breeze. What was it Jesse had called that particular mixture of smells? Southern romance, that was it.

Kate sighed again and plopped down into one of the chairs, wondering dismally what was going to become of her own Southern romance.

Was it going to prove to be as ephemeral as the fragrance of jasmine on the summer air?

It was certainly beginning to look that way. In the four days—*and nights*, she thought, *let's not forget the nights!*—of the most intimate relationship she'd ever experienced, the man involved had failed to make one single mention of even the possibility of a future together.

Not that she expected talk of commitment and marriage, not at this stage. It would have been nice, of course, now that she knew that's what she wanted, but she didn't expect it. She had, however, expected some small indication that he wanted this affair, or relationship, or whatever they were indulging in, to go on for some unspecified length of time. Some hint of curiosity about what her plans might be. Some flexing of the masculine prerogative she'd given him by becoming his lover. Some reasonable amount of interest in where all this time together was leading.

"Oh, hell," she said aloud, disgusted with herself.

She didn't want reasonableness! Not by a long shot. What she wanted was for Jesse to come charging after her with declarations of undying love and threats of mayhem and murder if she wouldn't marry him immediately.

It was apparently her curse, she thought irritably, to be one of that unfashionable breed of women who wanted their man to stake his claim in no uncertain terms.

Isn't that what she'd wished Reed would do? Come charging down from Boston and drag her back by the hair to prove he loved her?

Wishful thinking all around. She obviously wasn't the type to inspire men to rash acts of passion on her behalf.

She toed off her sandals, slouching in the balcony chair, and hoisted her feet onto the wrought-iron railing to sulk about the unfairness of life and modern mating rituals.

"Where the hell's my drink?" she grumbled, completely disregarding all she'd ever learned about grace under pressure.

She was so engrossed in her dismal thoughts that she didn't hear the knock on the hotel room door, or the holler of "Room service" when the knock wasn't answered.

Reed came out of the bathroom at the second knock. "Drinks are here," he said, calling to Kate as he headed for the door with his shirt hanging open and a towel dangling from his hand.

JESSE SPENT about fifteen minutes telling himself he was overreacting and another ten letting Lilac tell him the same thing.

"Don't be silly, Jesse," she said. "Kate wasn't ashamed for you to meet her aunt Katherine. She was just a bit apprehensive, is all." Lilac gave a delicate little shiver. "That woman has the sharpest tongue of anyone I ever met, and she isn't the least bit shy about using it. I'm sure Kate was real impressed with the way you handled her. I know I was."

Jesse gave her a look.

"Well, I was," Lilac insisted. "And you're wrong about her ex-fiancé, too. Kate isn't the least bit interested in Reed Sullivan. She never has been."

"She was engaged to him, for God's sake!"

"Yes, well, but that was just a little misunderstandin', is all."

Jesse glared at her. "Some misunderstanding," he barked, and then was immediately contrite. "I'm sorry, darlin'," he said, taking her hands in his. "It's not you I'm mad at, it's Kate."

"Well, don't be," Lilac advised. "Kate's in love with you."

Quick hope flared in his chest. "Did she tell you that?" he asked eagerly.

"Well . . . no, not exactly."

His face fell.

"But Kate isn't the kind to wear her heart on her sleeve," Lilac said. "You know how Yankees are. Kind of cold-natured. Not," she hastened to assure him, "that Kate is cold-natured or anythin'. She's just—"

But Jesse wasn't really listening. *No,* he was thinking, *Kate isn't cold-natured at all. Not by any stretch of the imagination!* She was sweet and warm and loving, with the right man. With him.

So why hadn't she uttered a single word of love, even when he'd had her begging for completion in his arms? And why had she looked at him as if she was ashamed to have him meet her aunt? And how could she possibly, at this very minute, even dare to be thinking of letting herself be persuaded to go back to Boston and marry her hand-picked fiancé when it was obvious to Jesse that the man was all wrong for her? Reed Sullivan didn't know a goddamn thing about the real Kate!

Besides, she was in love with Jesse, whether she knew it or not!

"I won't let it happen," Jesse said.

"Won't let what happen, honey?" Lilac said softly, with something of the air of a woman talking to a suddenly deranged individual. He was squeezing the blood out of her fingers.

"Nothing." Jesse smiled at her. "Nothing for you to worry about, Lilac, darlin'." He loosened his grip and lifted her hands to his lips in mute apology. "Nothing at all," he said, more himself now that he'd decided what needed to be done.

He'd been far too easy-going with Kate. That was the problem. Far too subtle in his courtship of her. He'd forgotten she was a Yankee, Boston-bred, practical to a fault and obviously not in tune with all the delicate nuances of a Southern courtship.

Nice and easy was good and well, but some women just had to be hit over the head with a club before they knew who they belonged to.

"YOU GO FINISH getting dressed," Kate said, getting up as she finally became aware that someone was pounding on the hotel door. "I'll get it."

They reached the door at just about the same instant.

"Go on," Kate said, pulling it open. "I'll bring your martini to you in the bath—" Her eyes grew round with delighted surprise. "Jesse! What are you doing here?"

He pushed past the startled bellboy, stalking into the room like a prowling cougar who'd been deprived of his prey and was ready to pounce on the first thing that moved, out of pure cussedness. He eyed the disheveled Reed with undisguised antagonism before turning his full attention to Kate. The fact that both her shoulders and her feet were bare didn't improve his temper in the least. "The question is," he drawled, "what are *you* doing here?" The words were heavy with innuendo.

Kate's delight slid toward indignation. "I don't think I like the tone of that question, Mr. de Vallerin," she said imperiously.

"I don't much care whether you like my tone or not. I don't like you being here, alone, with him." His tone was low, intimate and menacing. His eyes were blue flames of pure masculine possessiveness. "What do you think of that, Miz Hightower?"

Oh, God, she thought, *I love it!*

But she certainly couldn't admit it; after all, she had her reputation as a Hightower to think of. Not to mention the honor of her entire sex. If she let him get away with a stunt like this now, she'd be putting up with macho nonsense for the rest of her life.

She sniffed, as if totally unimpressed, and stuck her nose in the air. "Not much," she said, challenging him.

He reached out and put his hand on the back of her neck, catching her hair very gently in his fist. "Am I going to have to drag you out of here?"

Kate nearly melted into a warm, whimpering heap of female submissiveness in the middle of the hotel's pale gold rug. "If you think you can," she said, tossing her head so that his hand fell away.

"Oh, I can, all right." Before she could make another move, or think to evade him, Jesse crouched, pressing his shoulder into her stomach, and hoisted her over his shoulder.

Kate squealed with excitement and delicious fear. This was more than she'd dared hope for and ten times better than she'd imagined! She grabbed the strapless bodice of her dress with one hand, struggling to hold it in place, while she hit him—carefully—with the other. "Put me down," she demanded, just to see what he'd do next.

"Hold still." He smacked her bottom. "And shut up."

Thrilled, Kate shut up.

"I'm sorry if this makes you unhappy," Jesse said to Reed, "but Kate's mine. You had your chance with her and you blew it. You don't get another one." He held out his hand. "No hard feelings, I hope?"

Grinning, Reed shook it. "No hard feelings," he said.

"My shoes," Kate sputtered as Jesse hefted her weight and headed for the door. "My purse. Jesse, let me at least get my purse."

Reed handed her her purse as she passed him. "Good luck, Kate," he said and closed the door after them.

"Jesse, you can put me down now," Kate said as he continued down the hall. "Jesse, this isn't funny anymore. You can put me down. Jesse!"

Oh, Lord, what if someone saw them? Romance was all well and good but she'd die of embarrassment if anyone saw him carrying her like this. A Hightower of Boston, being hauled through a hotel corridor like a sack of flour!

She hit him on the bottom with her purse. "Jesse!"

He ignored her and stabbed the elevator call button.

The doors slid open.

Kate heard a woman's giggle.

"That's the way to do it, son," a man said as two couples walked off the elevator and into the hall.

"I'm going to kill you for this, Jesse de Vallerin," Kate promised, covering her face with her purse as he carried her into the elevator.

It was, thankfully, empty.

Kate felt her bottom hit the wall and then Jesse bent slightly, letting her slide to her bare feet. He leaned into her, holding her there as they straightened. "Good Lord, woman, you weigh a ton!" he said and fastened his mouth to hers.

Kate dropped her purse and threw her arms around his neck, melting like powdered sugar on his tongue.

The elevator doors opened and closed twice, leaving them the only passengers both times, before they finally came up for air.

"I'm sorry," Jesse said against her lips. "I don't know what came over me, acting like some caveman—" he buried his face in the soft, fragrant skin of her neck "—God, I thought I was losing you."

"No, don't apologize. I'm glad you acted like a caveman." Kate took his face between her hands, bringing his eyes to hers. "Because until you did, I thought you didn't want me."

"Not want you?" Jesse looked at her as if he couldn't believe what he'd heard. "Good Lord, woman, what's a man got to do to get through to you?"

Kate giggled from pure happiness. "I think you just did it."

Jesse grinned. His slow, wicked, lady-killing grin. "It's just like I thought," he drawled, "you Yankee women just don't understand the subtle approach to courtship."

"Is that what you've been doing, Jesse, courting me?"

He kissed her softly. "Couldn't you tell?"

Kate shook her head. "You didn't say."

"Well, darlin', I'm saying it now," he teased. And then his expression turned absolutely, perfectly, solemnly serious. He reached into his jacket pocket, pulled out a small, ring-sized box and flipped it open with his thumb. "I love you, Kate. And I want you to marry me."

"Oh, Jesse." Her eyes filled with happy tears. "I love you, too. So much."

"Well, hey, darlin'. It's nothing to cry about." He took her left hand, slipped the ring onto her finger and then kissed it into place. "Come on now, darlin'. Don't cry." He kissed her tenderly, brushing his lips over hers. Once. Twice. A third time. And then again, more forcefully. Pinning her against the wall with the weight of his body, he brought his hand up to cover the inviting swell of her breast.

Kate responded by wrapping both arms around his neck and straining against him with every fiber of her being. When he lifted his head, there wasn't a tear in sight.

"Guess I'm going to have to brush up on my tough-guy technique," he said lovingly, teasing her about her heated response to his caveman tactics.

Kate smiled seductively. "As long as you don't forget all that easy lovin' you're so good at," she purred and pulled his head down for another kiss.

Several long, heated, breathless seconds later, they were forced apart by the sound of smothered laughter and voices.

Kate peeked over Jesse's shoulder. "Oh, dear," she said, looking at the half dozen or so people waiting to get into the elevator. "We've been caught." She hid her face in his shoulder as the elevator filled.

"Going up?" someone inquired politely.

"Yes, please," Jesse said, as composed as if he weren't holding a blushing, barefoot woman in his arms. "Sixteenth floor."

"My reputation is ruined," Kate moaned into his neck. "No Hightower has ever been caught necking. It's just not done."

"Oh, Lord," said Jesse, as if a terrible thought had just occurred to him. "Does that mean I have to explain myself to your great-aunt Katherine?"

Epilogue

THE WEDDING WAS HELD three months later in Jack and Aimée Butterfield's garden, amid a forest of flowers and nearly two hundred happy, laughing guests. It was nothing like the sedate, understated ceremony that had been canceled in Boston.

There were children present, for one thing. All of Jesse's nieces and nephews, the children of his second cousins once removed, the babies of friends and every Hightower child Kate had been able to convince her relatives to bring to her wedding. Instead of beautifully assembled canapés and two choices of entrées for a sit-down dinner at the country club, there was a sumptuous buffet of shrimp Creole, spicy jambalaya, two kinds of gumbo and traditional red beans and rice catered by Cliff's. Two bartenders served up mint juleps, rum punch coolers and Dixie beer along with the French champagne that would have been served in Boston. Instead of the country club band playing popular tunes there was a Cajun band in the front parlor where the rugs had been taken up for dancing, a small jazz ensemble on the sun porch for listening and violins to accompany the bride down the aisle.

Laura Butterfield and her cousin Carey Lyn preceded the maid of honor, solemnly sprinkling fragrant flower petals and making sure Jesse's youngest nephew didn't dawdle in his duties as ring bearer. Lilac happily exchanged her simple blue A-line gown and tiny veiled hat for a bell-skirted dress of palest lavender silk organdy and a flower-bedecked picture hat. And Kate equally happy forgot all about the tailored satin sheath and elbow-length veil she'd been intending to wear for Reed and searched New Orleans for the most romantic wedding gown she could find.

There were ahs of delight and approval as she floated down the flower-strewn aisle in a tight-waisted, off-the-shoulder gown of ivory silk, with huge puffed sleeves and a wide, swaying skirt. Her frothy, floor-length tulle veil was anchored over her curling, unbound hair by a circlet of tiny white jasmine and orange blossoms. Her bridal bouquet, picked by Jesse that morning, was made up of the freshest, most fragrant flowers in his sister's garden.

He stood waiting for her at the end of the aisle, looking like a modern-day version of a riverboat gambler in pale gray trousers, a snug-fitting darker gray vest under a cream-colored frock coat and a fine white lawn shirt with a discreet spill of lace at the collar and cuffs. His diamond earring glittered in the bright afternoon sun, almost as bright as the smile he gave his bride as he accepted her hand from that of her father.

There were more ahs and murmurs of feminine wistfulness when Jesse unselfconsciously raised his bride's fingers to his lips before tucking them into the crook of his arm as they turned to face the priest.

And then, "Dearly beloved," the priest began, and everyone became reverently still as two people gladly, joyously joined their lives together.

The ring Jesse slid on her finger was a simple gold band, engraved on the inside with their initials and the date, an exact match for the larger one she slipped onto his finger. An exact match, too, for the gold hoop she halted the ceremony to fasten in his ear. Reaching up, she removed the diamond stud, handed it to a grinning Lilac and replaced it with the tiny gold hoop.

She pulled his head down to kiss it into place. "I love you, Jesse," she whispered into his ear.

"And I love you," he said, turning his head to capture her lips with his.

The priest cleared his throat. "You can't kiss the bride yet," he said, as Jesse drew Kate into his arms to take the kiss deeper. "I haven't pronounced you husband and wife."

Jesse lifted his head slightly, turning to look at the priest as if to say, "Well?" and waited.

The assembled guests tittered.

The priest gave them all a mock stern look, waiting until they'd quieted down and Jesse and Kate were once again properly facing him. "I now pronounce you husband and wife," he intoned solemnly. "And now, Mr. de Vallerin," he added, his eyes twinkling, "you may kiss your bride."

And Jesse did. Thoroughly, completely, with such exquisite tenderness that even Great-Aunt Katherine Hightower was seen to lift a pressed Irish linen handkerchief to the corner of her eye.

HARLEQUIN®

Don't miss these Harlequin favorites by some of our most distinguished authors!
And now, you can receive a discount by ordering two or more titles!

HT #25663	THE LAWMAN by Vicki Lewis Thompson	$3.25 U.S.☐/$3.75 CAN. ☐
HP #11788	THE SISTER SWAP by Susan Napier	$3.25 U.S.☐/$3.75 CAN. ☐
HR #03293	THE MAN WHO CAME FOR CHRISTMAS by Bethany Campbell	$2.99 U.S.☐/$3.50 CAN. ☐
HS #70667	FATHERS & OTHER STRANGERS by Evelyn Crowe	$3.75 U.S.☐/$4.25 CAN. ☐
HI #22198	MURDER BY THE BOOK by Margaret St. George	$2.89 ☐
HAR #16520	THE ADVENTURESS by M.J. Rodgers	$3.50 U.S.☐/$3.99 CAN. ☐
HH #28885	DESERT ROGUE by Erin Yorke	$4.50 U.S.☐/$4.99 CAN. ☐

(limited quantities available on certain titles)

	AMOUNT	$
DEDUCT:	**10% DISCOUNT FOR 2+ BOOKS**	$
ADD:	**POSTAGE & HANDLING**	$
	($1.00 for one book, 50¢ for each additional)	
	APPLICABLE TAXES**	$_____
	TOTAL PAYABLE	$_____
	(check or money order—please do not send cash)	

To order, complete this form and send it, along with a check or money order for the total above, payable to Harlequin Books, to: **In the U.S.:** 3010 Walden Avenue, P.O. Box 9047, Buffalo, NY 14269-9047; **In Canada:** P.O. Box 613, Fort Erie, Ontario, L2A 5X3.

Name: _____

Address: _____ City: _____

State/Prov.: _____ Zip/Postal Code: _____

**New York residents remit applicable sales taxes.
  Canadian residents remit applicable GST and provincial taxes.   HBACK-JS3

Look us up on-line at: http://www.romance.net

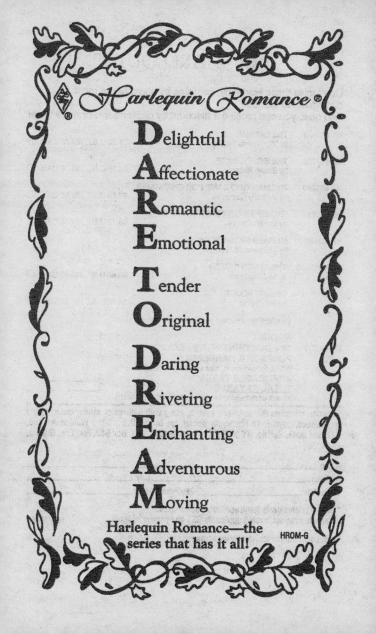

Harlequin Romance ®

Delightful

Affectionate

Romantic

Emotional

Tender

Original

Daring

Riveting

Enchanting

Adventurous

Moving

Harlequin Romance—the
series that has it all!

HROM-G

HARLEQUIN ✦ PRESENTS®

HARLEQUIN PRESENTS
men you won't be able to resist falling in love with...

HARLEQUIN PRESENTS
women who have feelings just like your own...

HARLEQUIN PRESENTS
powerful passion in exotic international settings...

HARLEQUIN PRESENTS
intense, dramatic stories that will keep you turning
to the very last page...

HARLEQUIN PRESENTS
The world's bestselling romance series!

Harlequin® Historical

If you're a serious fan of historical romance, then you're in luck!

Harlequin Historicals brings you stories by bestselling authors, rising new stars and talented first-timers.

Ruth Langan & Theresa Michaels
Mary McBride & Cheryl St. John
Margaret Moore & Merline Lovelace
Julie Tetel & Nina Beaumont
Susan Amarillas & Ana Seymour
Deborah Simmons & Linda Castle
Cassandra Austin & Emily French
Miranda Jarrett & Suzanne Barclay
DeLoras Scott & Laurie Grant...

You'll never run out of favorites.

Harlequin Historicals...they're too good to miss!

HH-GEN

HARLEQUIN®

I N T R I G U E ®

THAT'S INTRIGUE—DYNAMIC ROMANCE AT ITS BEST!

Harlequin Intrigue is now bringing you more—more men and mystery, more desire and danger. If you've been looking for thrilling tales of contemporary passion and sensuous love stories with taut, edge-of-the-seat suspense—then you'll *love* Harlequin Intrigue!

Every month, you'll meet four new heroes who are guaranteed to make your spine tingle and your pulse pound. With them you'll enter into the exciting world of Harlequin Intrigue—where your life is on the line and so is your heart!

Harlequin Intrigue—we'll leave you breathless!

INT-GEN

WAYS TO *UNEXPECTEDLY* MEET MR. RIGHT:

♡ *Go out with the sexy-sounding stranger your daughter secretly set you up with through a personal ad.*

♡ *RSVP yes to a wedding invitation—soon it might be your turn to say "I do!"*

♡ *Receive a marriage proposal by mail— from a man you've never met....*

These are just a few of the unexpected ways that written communication leads to love in Silhouette Yours Truly.

Each month, look for two fast-paced, fun and flirtatious Yours Truly *novels (with entertaining treats and sneak previews in the back pages) by some of your favorite authors—and some who are sure to become favorites.*

YOURS TRULY™:
Love—when you least expect it!

YT-GEN

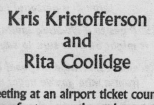

Kris Kristofferson
and
Rita Coolidge

A chance meeting at an airport ticket counter marked the beginning of a transcontinental romance between Kris Kristofferson and Rita Coolidge. She was on her way to Memphis. He was going to Nashville. Kris wasted no time in rerouting his flight to Memphis.

Theirs was a whirlwind love affair that marched them right down the aisle in 1973.

Unfortunately, the marriage ended in divorce a few years later.

B-KRIS